PRESTIGE PUZZLES

CROSSWORD

hinkler

Published by Hinkler Books Pty Ltd
45–55 Fairchild Street
Heatherton Victoria 3202 Australia
www.hinkler.com.au

Cover Design: Hinkler Studio
Typesetting: MPS Limited
Prepress: Graphic Print Group

ISBN: 978 1 7418 4068 4067 4

Printed and bound in China

PUZZLES

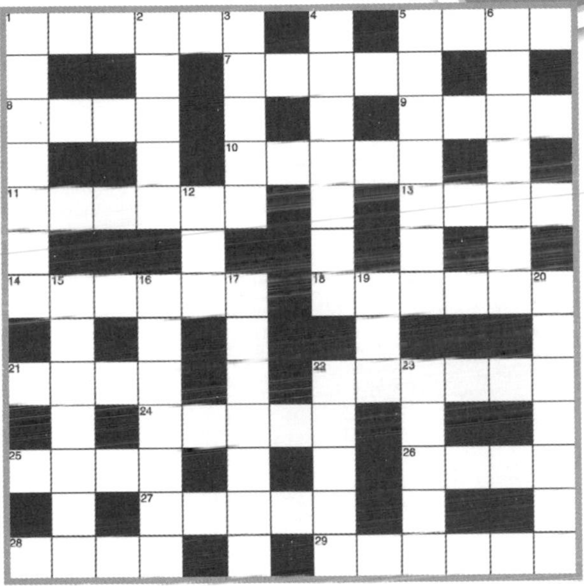

ACROSS

1. Excessively
5. Largest mammal, ... whale
7. Degrade
8. Forearm bone
9. Unable to hear
10. Store away greedily
11. Consequence
13. Tropical wading bird
14. Carnivores, meat ...
18. Bean or pea
21. Verbal
22. Surrendering
24. Mental picture
25. Computer part, silicon ...
26. Opinion survey
27. Hosiery
28. Fencing sword
29. Bestows

DOWN

1. Four-stringed guitar
2. Consumption
3. Sailing boat
4. Burnt sugar
5. Sheets & blankets
6. Radioactive element
12. Train carriage
15. Zeppelin
16. Blocking out of sun
17. Relieve itch
19. Supplement, ... out
20. Inundates
22. Stop
23. Drugged (horse)

CROSSWORD 2

ACROSS

1. Chaste
5. Canned fish
7. Lacking sensation
8. Dormant
9. Commands
12. Veers
15. Of the stomach
19. Crunchy stalk vegetable
21. Mercifully
22. Unconscious state
23. Cult
24. Colonists

DOWN

1. Retailer
2. Dining surface
3. Leaves out
4. Unlit area
5. Hitch
6. Rectifies
10. Grows faint
11. Crowd sound
12. Animal pouch
13. Simplicity
14. Windmill arm
15. Deep cuts
16. School absconder
17. Lazy people
18. Detour round
19. Church cellar
20. Regional

ACROSS

1. Gold or tin
7. Orators
8. Precious stone
10. Mused
12. Complete disorder
14. Soap foam
16. Historical periods
17. Purged
20. Ostentatious
23. To the fore
24. Restate (position)
25. Spry

DOWN

1. Army officers
2. Mimicked
3. Rushed
4. Removed
5. Refund
6. Stage whispers
9. Young sheep
11. Twin-hulled boat
13. Snake-like fish
15. Steam-room
16. Attempt
18. Lag behind
19. Deep chasm
21. Wool
22. Lout

CROSSWORD 4

ACROSS

1. Lowered in quality
4. Tapering fruit
7. Four-sided shapes
8. Annual periods
9. Fable
12. Partaking of liquor
15. Reminder token
17. Covered with cloth
18. Aristocratic
21. Responded
22. Lagoons
23. Impair

DOWN

1. Impasse
2. Strolled
3. Wild beasts' lairs
4. Small bunch of flowers
5. Water-related
6. Prosecutes
10. Backless couch
11. Waned
13. Direction
14. Reversal in progress
16. Filming machine
18. Not binding
19. Makes slip-up
20. Exalt

ACROSS

1. Yellow fruit
5. Stack
7. Russian liquor
8. Cleanse
9. Castle water ditch
10. Single entities
11. Steam-pressed
13. Udder tip
14. Side dishes
18. Pixie
21. Long movie
22. Decipher
24. Astonish
25. Small lake
26. Manage
27. Older person
28. Wooden barrels
29. Produces

DOWN

1. Laments
2. Pale with shock
3. Avert
4. Verb modifiers
5. Pet rodent
6. Inflexible
12. Culminate
15. Sanction
16. Shopping walkways
17. Threads
19. Pastry meal
20. Embroidery holes
22. Denounce
23. Recurrent period

CROSSWORD 6

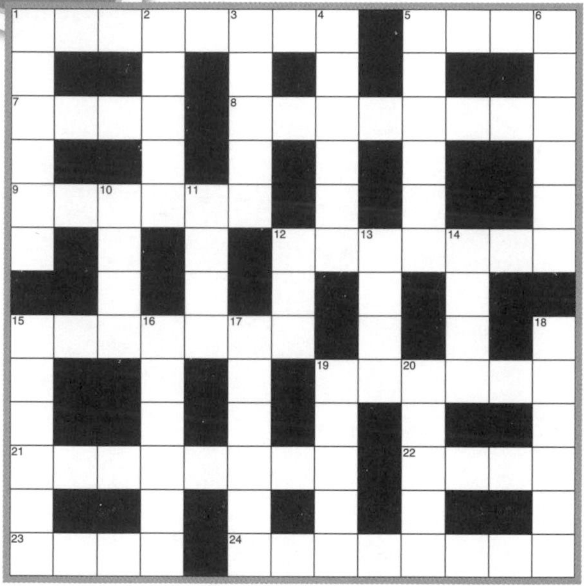

ACROSS

1. Fracture
5. Strike (toe)
7. Ogled
8. Strange
9. Abhor
12. Invents
15. Educator
19. Baboon or macaque
21. Stretch
22. The ... of Capri
23. Lofty
24. Naughtiness

DOWN

1. Type of insect
2. Business books review
3. Orchard fruit
4. Engraver
5. Spittle
6. Mooring spots
10. Zone
11. Actor, ... Grant
12. Aggressive dog
13. Resounding noise
14. Confiscated
15. Separate out (wheat)
16. Boxing hold
17. Mummify
18. Me
19. Fulfils (demand)
20. Horse's cry

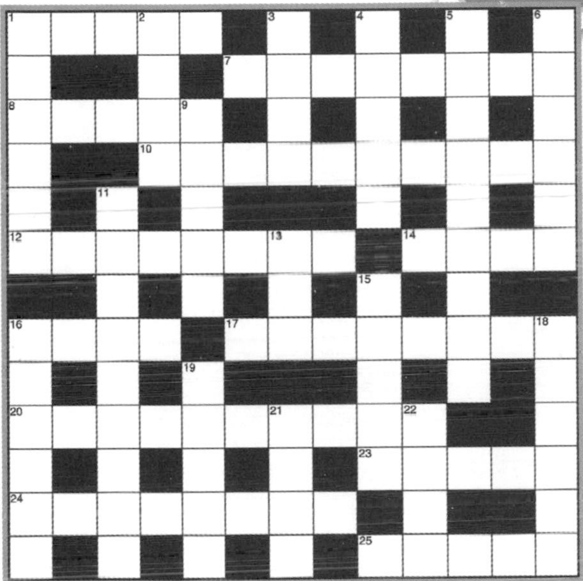

ACROSS

1. Jury
7. Dampness of air
8. Ballet skirts
10. Portable stairs
12. Roofs with straw
14. Expired
16. Submerged
17. Evangelist
20. Logos
23. Dog's cries
24. Regretfully
25. Performed slalom

DOWN

1. Powerful
2. Australian birds
3. Hindquarters
4. Travel permits
5. Retrospective wisdom
6. Crossbreed
9. Shop supplies
11. Cloud moisture
13. Wheat spike
15. Tall & skinny
16. Parody
18. Elevated
19. Lists of meals
21. Competently
22. Search for

CROSSWORD 8

ACROSS

1. Closer (of fit)
4. Coronet
7. Enforce solitude on
8. Attain
9. Of race & culture
12. Weigh up
15. Control
17. Unchanging
18. Plucked string sound
21. Makes a difference to
22. Ocean phases
23. Lifesaver

DOWN

1. Meddled
2. Watering by tube
3. Peruse
4. Cake layer
5. Yearbook
6. Curved entrance
10. Red wood
11. Sends by telephone
13. Instructor
14. Pierced with spear
16. Stratagem
18. Stretched firm
19. Spaces (between)
20. A great way off

ACROSS

1. Inn
5. Creep (towards)
7. Written tests
8. Leer
9. Acceptable
10. Skewered meat
11. Angry crowds
13. Absent
14. Harm
18. Dress ribbons
21. Brass instrument
22. Stood on hind legs
24. Public square
25. Canvas dwelling
26. Despicable
27. Do well (at)
28. Tinted
29. Non-liquids

DOWN

1. Fitted with cogs
2. Edit (text)
3. Slender bottle tops
4. Hare relatives
5. Pressure lines on map
6. False pretence
12. Unborn chick
15. Sharply
16. Changed suitably
17. Improve
19. Beer
20. Makes unhappy
22. Train tracks
23. Blacksmith's block

CROSSWORD 10

ACROSS

1. Sinew
5. Post of doorway
7. Had to repay
8. Public speeches
9. Personify
12. Clearness
15. Most considerate
19. Was unsuccessful
21. Purgative
22. Leak out
23. Open valley
24. Paraffin oil

DOWN

1. Hooped
2. Of hearing
3. Black wood
4. Ride
5. Furniture maker
6. Industriously
10. Coffee seed
11. Eat
12. Carve
13. Charismatic glow
14. Object of worship
15. Assassinated
16. Prescribed amount
17. Decrease in size
18. Stick (to)
19. More independent
20. Symbolic pictures

ACROSS

1. Pinch & twist
7. Cocktails
8. Shroud
10. Sixtieth, ..., eightieth
12. Biting
14. Imaginative plan
16. String tangle
17. Put in order
20. Cosmetics
23. Brazilian dance
24. Flowed out (from)
25. Pumped through tube

DOWN

1. Powerful businessman
2. Unfortunately
3. Turn towards
4. Declaim
5. Weaker competitors
6. Respiratory disorder
9. Ships' spines
11. Of the stomach
13. Neither
15. Is brave enough
16. Baby cat
18. Insist on
19. Sum up
21. Coral bank
22. Hindu garment

CROSSWORD 12

ACROSS

1. Opening
4. Proverb
7. Less abundant
8. Remove completely
9. Delivered, ... over
12. Cellophane covers
15. Role models
17. Harrowing ordeal
18. Compass point
21. Oblivious
22. Bread-raising agent
23. Suited

DOWN

1. Surpassed in excellence
2. Building's exterior
3. Every single
4. Land unit
5. Displayed
6. Alternatively, or ...
10. Live
11. Hips to ribs region
13. Exerted (oneself)
14. Spice
16. Textile, woven ...
18. Admiral's command
19. Stalk prey
20. Coconut tree

ACROSS

1. Calm
5. Be an omen of
7. Tremor
8. Caribbean nation
9. Travel by sea
10. Diminish
11. Harrowing trial
13. Prepare (manuscript)
14. African wildlife tour
18. Shocked
21. Essential part
22. Lashed
24. Foolish
25. Rub lightly
26. Baked treat
27. Use dragnet
28. Depend
29. Cruel person

DOWN

1. Subdivisions
2. Rouse
3. Match
4. Tropical disease
5. Implore
6. Cow farms
12. What we breathe
15. Aviation company
16. Nervous tension
17. Large lizards
19. Congeal
20. Neatest
22. Chops to ground
23. Shorted out

CROSSWORD 14

ACROSS
1. Christmas season
5. Hornet home
7. Not any
8. Medieval farm workers
9. Of the soil
12. Joyful
15. Peppered (with holes)
19. Flower syrup
21. Offensiveness
22. Roman robe
23. On the summit of
24. Vacations

DOWN
1. Pulled sharply
2. Incident
3. Suggest
4. Tooth coating
5. Subtle difference
6. Tuft of threads
10. Orange skin
11. Cure
12. Deity
13. Outside limit
14. Rapid
15. Hat-weaving leaves
16. Lump of food
17. Embroil
18. Thick lotions
19. Of the nose
20. Mentioned as example

ACROSS

1. Humiliated
4. Placed in an aviary
7. Real
8. Deceptive move
9. Mutilated
12. Green gems
15. Leave place of danger
17. Clambered up
18. Corn husks
21. Relaxation time
22. Lifting device
23. Slavery

DOWN

1. Put together
2. Warning bells
3. Barrel
4. Young cow
5. Largest primate
6. Song for two voices
10. Prohibit
11. Annoys
13. Combination of symptoms
14. Card game
16. Excluded
18. Smartly-groomed
19. Duct
20. Arm or leg

CROSSWORD 16

ACROSS

1. Vegetable tuber
5. Warmth
7. Absurd
8. Lumpy growth
9. Twofold
10. Mouth sore
11. Matter
13. Tallies
14. Spooned (out)
18. Locating
21. Grew old
22. Dines sumptuously
24. Tropical fruit
25. Genuine
26. A single time
27. Coral banks
28. ... or evens
29. Dodges (duty)

DOWN

1. Elton John hit, ... Wizard
2. Sports stadium
3. Take place
4. Emerges from egg
5. Water outlet
6. Leave (sinking ship)
12. Glacial material
15. Infuriated
16. Accounts records
17. Decomposed
19. Fury
20. Sealants
22. Misleading
23. Smell

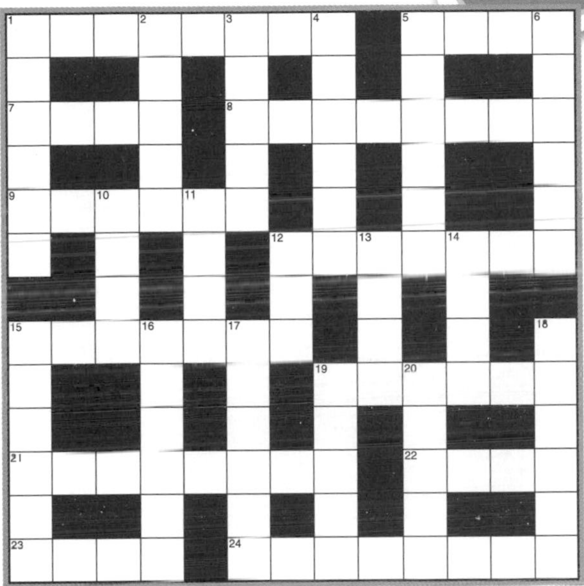

ACROSS

1. Orders
5. Green gemstone
7. Reservoir
8. Insulin-deficient person
9. Alternate ones
12. Spanned
15. Char
19. Get free
21. Hollow out
22. Wild cat
23. Compass point
24. Abandoned

DOWN

1. Universe
2. Canadian leaf symbol
3. Artist's naked models
4. Ice performer
5. Mocked
6. Go too far
10. Hawaiian dance
11. Peril
12. Receptacle
13. Charged particles
14. Carnival
15. Gentle wind
16. Deep blue pigment
17. Enlarge
18. Held for trial, on ...
19. Pitchers
20. Playful skip

CROSSWORD 18

ACROSS

1. Raided
4. Tin or iron
7. Ocean-liner waiter
8. Greatly please
9. Yacht basin
12. Advantageously
15. Accompanied
17. Grab
18. Gentle prod
21. Catching (thief)
22. Timidly
23. Walks wearily

DOWN

1. Very personal
2. Achieve
3. College supervisor
4. Style
5. Wide pedal
6. Reside
10. Female relatives
11. Riverside plants
13. Face veils
14. Sourness
16. Arrived (of day)
18. Assents with head
19. Jealousy
20. Illegally help

ACROSS

1. Finally
5. Melt
7. Flooded (of decks)
8. New Zealand bird
9. Farewell gesture
10. Stage play
11. Fiction books
13. Ladder step
14. Sponged
18. Hurry
21. Pass lightly (over)
22. Vatican's St ... Basilica (5'1)
24. Unhealthily overweight
25. Troy star, Eric ...
26. Tumble
27. More agreeable
28. Dedicatory verses
29. Wept

DOWN

1. Compared
2. Double
3. Length units
4. Nasal fluid
5. Foils
6. Move ahead
12. Rest on bed
15. Ungainly
16. Laments
17. Wholesomeness
19. Unreturnable tennis serve
20. Lay snugly
22. Social equals
23. Ache

CROSSWORD 20

ACROSS

1. Small decorative object
5. Zodiac Cancer symbol
7. Barber's tool
8. Policy of non-violence
9. Leguminous plant
12. Said
15. Unspecified person
19. Discontinued
21. Living entity
22. Speed contest
23. Elephant group
24. Ingests

DOWN

1. Of the supernatural
2. Monastery head
3. Force out
4. Travel docket
5. Caffeine beverage
6. Jolted
10. Standard
11. Inside
12. Operation
13. Pipe
14. Purges
15. Not rough
16. Delivery task
17. War fleets
18. Vipers
19. Punctuation mark
20. Of hearing

ACROSS

1. Body part
7. Republic, ... & Tobago
8. Mythical story
10. Arctic vehicle
12. Slanting line
14. Unit of power
16. Office table
17. Beset
20. Inarticulate
23. Hanker
24. Working (dough)
25. Pay out (cash)

DOWN

1. Displease
2. Sickens
3. Forehead
4. Pungent bulb
5. To be recommended
6. Most lazy
9. Relish
11. Large-scale killings
13. Horse-like animal
15. Actor, ... DeVito
16. Thirst quenchers
18. Put on
19. Shadowy
21. Hire
22. Short-term worker

CROSSWORD 22

ACROSS

1. Untitled
4. Reproductive organ
7. Circus performer
8. Of past times
9. Provided with personnel
12. Thought of
15. Physically demanding
17. Rasping
18. Egg shapes
21. Fatigued
22. Singer, Buddy ...
23. Absorbed (water)

DOWN

1. Utmost
2. Climb
3. Adds soundtrack
4. Upon
5. Enduring
6. Tired reflex
10. Finger or toe
11. Giggle
13. Relied
14. Sun umbrella
16. Underground hollow
18. Solemn vow
19. Move to & fro
20. Money rolls

ACROSS

1. Infuriate
5. Shed tears
7. Filter
8. Long story
9. Mosquito bite irritation
10. Fossil resin
11. Apple, ... Smith
13. Dull
14. Ferocious
18. Partition
21. Current units
22. Dog breed
24. Move on knees
25. Relinquish (territory)
26. Dress-up toy
27. Velocity
28. Requests, ... for
29. Takes place after

DOWN

1. Flags
2. Anew
3. Short prose piece
4. Small stones
5. More peculiar
6. Parcel
12. Scold repeatedly
15. Without purpose
16. Infected sore
17. Encloses in shell
19. Reminder
20. Sewing spikes
22. Knife part
23. Assistants

CROSSWORD 24

ACROSS

1. Male voice
5. Out of harm's way
7. Shaving cut
8. Flying around (planet)
9. Pacify
12. New experience
15. More verdant
19. Numb
21. Supplied funds for
22. Mellow
23. Dip into drink
24. Surgeons' workplaces

DOWN

1. Expel from country
2. Vexed
3. Atmosphere layer
4. Plant seed part
5. Resolve
6. Nervously
10. Foundation
11. Atop
12. Neither
13. Ballot
14. Indecent
15. Hooked (fish) with pole
16. Venture forth
17. Evoke
18. Positive electrodes
19. Evade
20. Confess

ACROSS

1. Arctic (region)
7. Exonerated
8. Leg bone
10. Improve efficiency of
12. Proximity
14. Ewe's young
16. Dock
17. Clearly expressed
20. Trees retaining foliage
23. Rescued
24. More slender
25. Giant monsters

DOWN

1. Benefactor
2. Line of rotation
3. Gifted
4. Weaving machines
5. Evasion
6. Verb modifier
9. Make amends
11. Medical support worker
13. Gender
15. Tribal groups
16. Nauseated
18. Barters
19. Spy, secret ...
21. Optic organs
22. Performed in opera

CROSSWORD 26

ACROSS

1. Monotonous
4. Different
7. Sultan's wife
8. Restraining cord
9. Straighten
12. Inflame
15. One who solicits votes
17. Sliced very thinly
18. Duck's call
21. Finest
22. Oral sense
23. Of earthquakes

DOWN

1. Appeals board
2. Accustomed
3. Coal vein
4. Australian gemstone
5. Announces
6. Wealthy
10. Ledger entry
11. Satirical routines
13. Plague
14. Chafes
16. Stops momentarily
18. Give up
19. Leg joint
20. Flows away

ACROSS

1. Forward
5. Clock face
7. Glowing coal
8. Two-sided contest
9. Knowledge test
10. Paint layers
11. Sound of moving leaves
13. Looks upon
14. Sailing boats
18. Showers
21. Loud noise
22. Customs
24. Snow shelter
25. Departed
26. Tibetan monk
27. Sister's daughter
28. Early harp
29. Rattled

DOWN

1. Neat
2. Allocate
3. Tennis 40/40
4. Gains possession of
5. Kitchen cabinet
6. Police college
12. Illuminated
15. Human body study
16. Sanitation
17. Rebuked
19. Pod vegetable
20. Nourish
22. Family dwellings
23. Model-plane wood

CROSSWORD 28

ACROSS

1. More nauseous
5. Not stiff
7. Wicked
8. Walked unsteadily
9. Wrestle
12. Searched (body)
15. Doubt innocence of
19. Rode bicycle
21. Redraw
22. Fish breathing organ
23. (To) which person?
24. Small birds

DOWN

1. Expeditions
2. Collection of charts
3. Matter
4. Book user
5. Defames
6. Cushioned
10. Scatters (seeds)
11. Early guitar
12. Be the right size for
13. Very black
14. Execute
15. Misery
16. Cough mucus
17. Assertions
18. Grown-ups
19. Latin American hand drum
20. Tobacco product

ACROSS

1. Havoc
7. Beekeeper
8. Vocal sound
10. Manual art
12. Elegant
14. Honey drink
16. Boast
17. Undo
20. Available
23. Recorded (music)
24. Hugging
25. Used keyboard

DOWN

1. Exploring caverns
2. Exclamation of pain
3. Mimicked
4. Receive ball
5. Thin wires
6. Declared
9. Roof overhangs
11. Procession
13. Grecian vase
15. Gymnastics event
16. Tree limb
18. Required
19. Bible song
21. Taverns
22. Simple

CROSSWORD 30

ACROSS

1. Brass metal
5. Bird of prey
7. Aunt's husband
8. Propagated
9. Culinary delight
10. Lag behind
11. To wit
13. Pigmented eye membrane
14. Runway surface
18. Priesthood
21. Appear
22. Loop
24. Ultra manly
25. Volcanic rock
26. Earth
27. Depart
28. Bunks
29. Tended (patients)

DOWN

1. Display case
2. Chaplain
3. Corroded
4. Marine
5. Lower edge of skirt
6. Clothed in
12. Meadow (poetic)
15. Standard
16. Animals that suckle young
17. Cover up
19. Hawaiian garland
20. Capitulated
22. Assembly of witches
23. Leader

ACROSS

1. Most significant
5. Baking chamber
7. Appeal
8. Lack of response
9. Squeaks and rattles
12. Of the senses
15. Line of Chinese emperors
19. Higher-priced
21. Long-necked animals
22. Secluded place
23. Pecans or almonds
24. Arm/torso joint

DOWN

1. Staring open-mouthed
2. Collect
3. Leaves room
4. Hypnotic state
5. River creatures
6. Roman XC
10. Smooth out (shirt creases)
11. Shady trees
12. Recite
13. Letter
14. Across
15. Fire-breathing monster
16. Church tables
17. Robberies
18. Stocks & shares agent
19. 70s dance music
20. Declare void

CROSSWORD 32

ACROSS

1. Swellings
7. Interim
8. Perfect
10. Woven wall-hangings
12. Arriving at
14. Sweetly appealing
16. Spoilt child
17. Orators
20. Senselessly
23. Abated
24. Languidness
25. Cranium

DOWN

1. Dally
2. Fire fuel
3. Festival
4. Bring together
5. Made fun of
6. Leaseholder
9. Wood-shaping machine
11. Small parrots
13. Crab's pinch
15. Aesop tale
16. Wrist ornament
18. Summer shoe
19. Have buoyancy
21. Wise person
22. Tug sharply

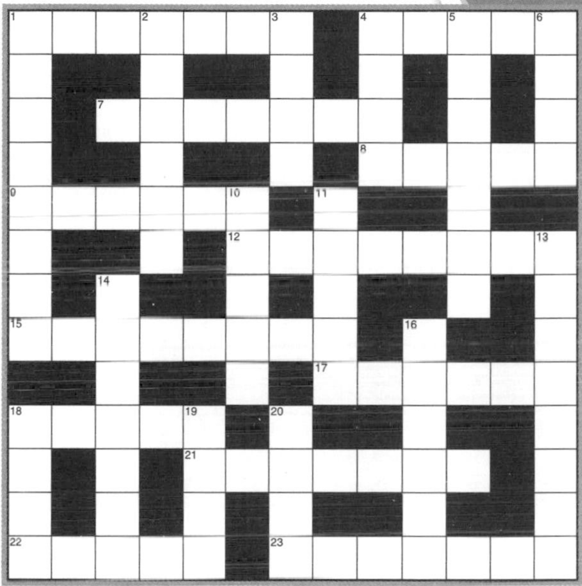

ACROSS

1. Left unoccupied
4. Metropolitan
7. Looked briefly
8. Unconcealed
9. Alpine melodies
12. Giving therapy to
15. Technical drawings
17. Howled shrilly
18. Singer, ... Sinatra
21. Slipped by
22. Estimate
23. Throat capsule

DOWN

1. Grape-growing property
2. Wartime friends
3. Ship's floor
4. Unbutton
5. Gain
6. Afterwards
10. Weasel-like creature
11. Untidy
13. Obtain degree
14. Flair
16. Claim
18. Adult tadpole
19. Lock openers
20. Lamenting cry

CROSSWORD 34

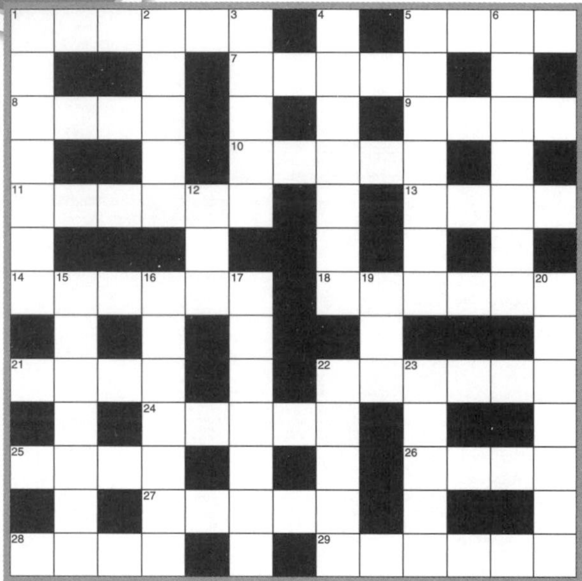

ACROSS

1. Dramatic conclusion
5. Pledges
7. Line-up
8. Matures
9. Shop light, ... sign
10. Gold bar
11. Maintenance
13. Compulsion
14. Young eagle
18. Insatiable
21. Feel sore
22. Ferret relative
24. Run after
25. Marine creature
26. Weight unit
27. Terminated
28. Poultry products
29. Public drains

DOWN

1. Characteristic
2. Gangway
3. Provide with gear
4. Meeting & joining
5. Enterprise
6. Treated unfairly
12. December 31, New Year's ...
15. Raising (eyebrows)
16. Blood-sucking worms
17. In the direction of
19. Cereal grass
20. Daffodil shades
22. Unwanted plants
23. Awry

ACROSS

1. Most useful
5. Parsley or sage
7. Wildebeests
8. Tolerable
9. Laden
12. Happened (upon)
15. Suffocated in water
19. Aimless stroll
21. Courted
22. Fairy's rod
23. Wearing footwear
24. Defrauded

DOWN

1. Greatly
2. Gave medicine to
3. Lodge firmly
4. Roofing grass
5. Utter bliss
6. Concocted
10. In addition
11. All square
12. Oily fish
13. Greenish blue
14. Rein in
15. Wreckage
16. Harry Potter is one
17. Ejects
18. Married
19. Diameter halves
20. Cut (lawn)

CROSSWORD 36

ACROSS

1. Oxen harnesses
7. Unable to be eaten
8. Unnerve
10. Punctuation marks
12. Barely
14. Travel pass
16. Table light
17. Ability
20. Benevolence
23. This planet
24. Gymnasts' garments
25. Out of bed

DOWN

1. Adolescents
2. Supplements, ... out
3. Against
4. Colloquial saying
5. Objectionable
6. Japanese hostess
9. Impart knowledge
11. Shuttlecock game
13. Sever (branches)
15. Remove soap from
16. Probable
18. One or the other
19. Dirt-free
21. Undressed
22. Drains

ACROSS

1. Visual trick, ... illusion
4. Conscious
7. Shortfall
8. Different
9. Lubricant
12. Small-style newspapers
15. Tip
17. Wriggle
18. Urge to action
21. Not balanced
22. Resided
23. Showed (to seat)

DOWN

1. Eager to please
2. Frozen polar cover
3. Good fortune
4. Singing voice
5. Antiquated
6. Pitcher
10. Moral principle
11. Follows directives
13. Boiled gently
14. Dracula is one
16. Undergo genetic change
18. Chilled
19. Strong desire
20. Restaurant list

CROSSWORD 38

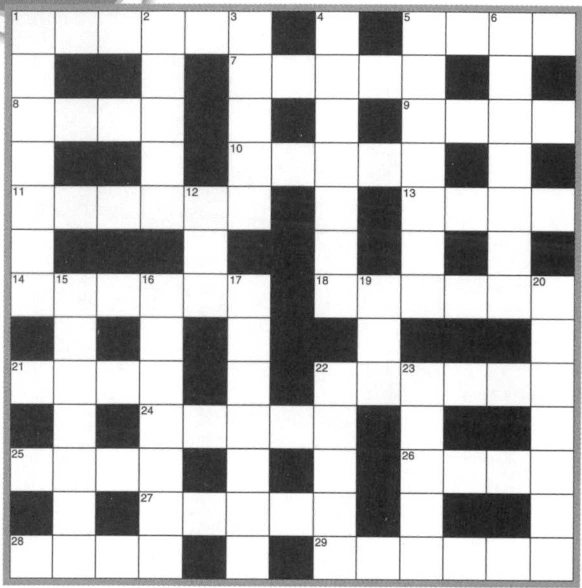

ACROSS

1. Recluse
5. Horizontal
7. Easy pace
8. Perfumed powder
9. Cries
10. Lawful
11. Equines
13. Immense periods
14. Intimidates
18. Cease
21. Statistics
22. Frothed
24. Alcove
25. White metal
26. Hard work
27. Dodge
28. Stitched garment edges
29. Wealthier

DOWN

1. Devised (plot)
2. Sneers
3. Pursues closely
4. Make off
5. Becomes septic
6. People devoid of pigment
12. Consume food
15. Greed
16. Subtle differences
17. Unique
19. Self-pride
20. Walking infant
22. High temperature
23. Loft

ACROSS

1. Paltry sum
5. Put up (painting)
7. Scruff (of neck)
8. Slow-moving reptile
9. Fireplace
12. Science subject
15. Traitor's crime
19. Made (wage)
21. Roaming stealthily
22. Jetty
23. Night sky object
24. Ragged

DOWN

1. South American cloak
2. Belonging to them
3. V-shaped cut
4. Improve in value
5. Animal feet
6. Extracts (information)
10. Wheel shaft
11. Adds (up)
12. Grenade trigger
13. Hindu meditation
14. Symbolic picture
15. Lures
16. Reply
17. Woodwind musician
18. Worshipped
19. Octet number
20. Pakistan currency

CROSSWORD 40

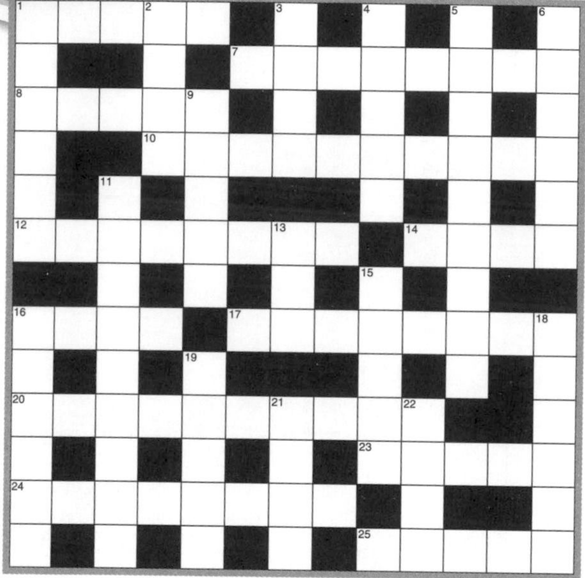

ACROSS

1. Majestic
7. Of bone system
8. Suites
10. Child's ride-on plank
12. Pining (for)
14. Glides on snow
16. Pastry case
17. Concealed
20. People in book
23. Gullible
24. Takes glory (from)
25. Moved sideways

DOWN

1. Uncommon event
2. Weaponry
3. Short comic sketch
4. Sphere
5. Aggressors
6. Razor parts
9. Smelly animal
11. Cloudy eye condition
13. Capture (criminal)
15. Squirrel nut
16. Building's exterior
18. Guard
19. Cold meal
21. Ballet dress
22. Beach material

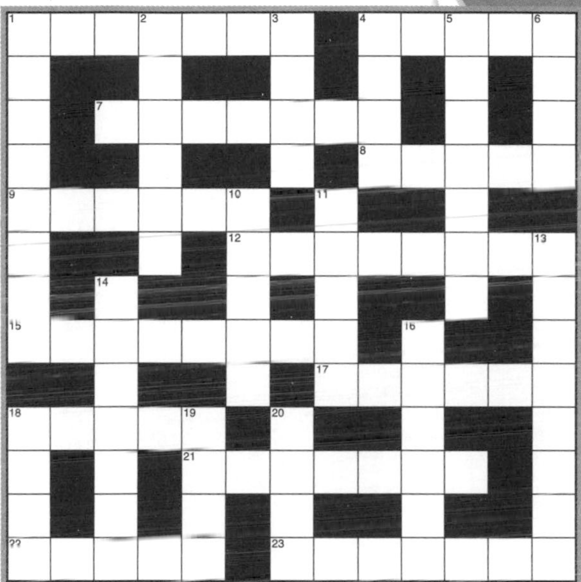

ACROSS

1. Postponed
4. Ventured
7. North American wild horse
8. Trap
9. Entertainment venue
12. Plodding
15. Incapacitated
17. Waned
18. Articulate
21. Took (revenge)
22. Cut into cubes
23. Newer

DOWN

1. Instructed
2. Maltreats
3. Haul
4. Poodles or terriers
5. Splendid clothes
6. Stun
10. Circular reef
11. Black & white mammal
13. Horticulturist
14. Clairvoyant
16. Menservants
18. Empty space
19. Heavy metal
20. Part of leg

CROSSWORD 42

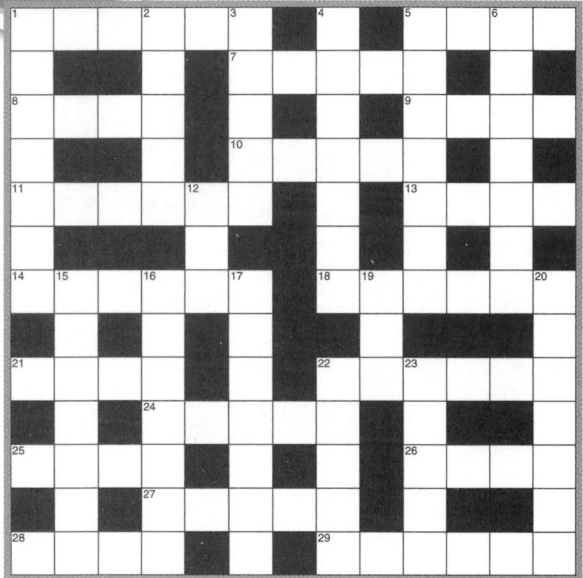

ACROSS

1. Surpass in auction
5. Well ventilated
7. Very annoyed
8. Prompted (actor)
9. Authentic
10. Cowboy's rope
11. Eagerly
13. Cook in water
14. Delicate
18. Striding
21. Wound blemish
22. Rang (of bells)
24. Tough plastic
25. Unaccompanied
26. Mocking remark
27. Callous opportunists
28. Sight organs
29. African scavengers

DOWN

1. Fruit tree grove
2. Waited, ... one's time
3. Faintly
4. White root vegetable
5. Of heart/lung exercises
6. Reconfigure
12. Tennis call on serve
15. Small, salted fish
16. Anxious
17. More youthful
19. Affirmative vote
20. Mechanical devices
22. Luxurious & expensive
23. Journalist's slant

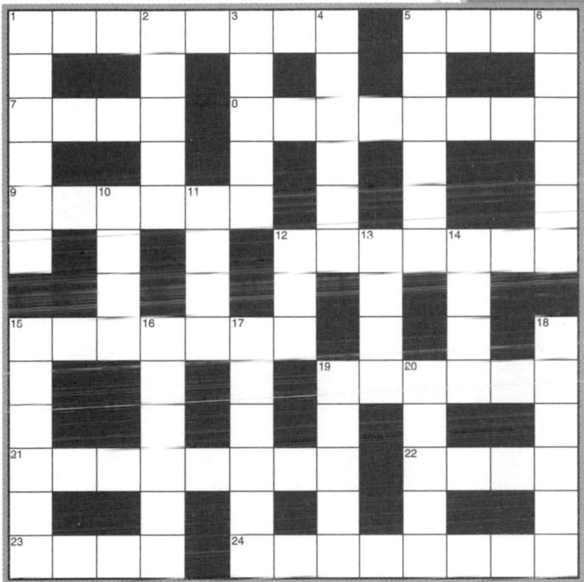

ACROSS

1. Tending to squander
5. Water-dripping sound
7. Twist
8. Sword sheath
9. Lasso loops
12. Accept
15. Floating debris
19. Most peculiar
21. Delivers sermon
22. Male monarch
23. Starchy tubers
24. Struggled against

DOWN

1. Stirring from sleep
2. Removes
3. Goes without food
4. Accountable
5. Tiny rock
6. Pool of rainwater
10. Greek liquor
11. Heads of corn
12. Brink
13. Lacking warmth
14. Indolent
15. Not rigid
16. Ordeals
17. Mooring weight
18. Put on (event)
19. Desert resting place
20. ... & duchesses

CROSSWORD 44

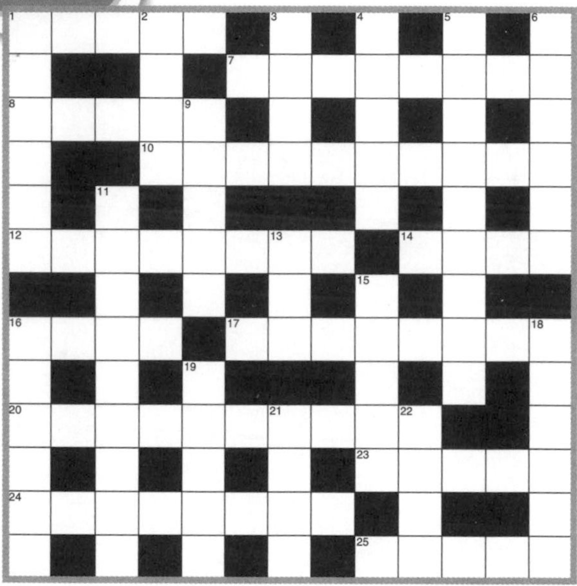

ACROSS

1. Flower segment
7. Envious
8. Involved tales
10. Environmental
12. More threadbare
14. Floating filth
16. Nuclear weapon, ... bomb
17. Depraved
20. Crockery
23. Brown photo shade
24. Octopus arm
25. Fire remains

DOWN

1. Wage recipients
2. Pimple rash
3. Implement
4. Rule (of monarch)
5. Brewed
6. Safe haven
9. Healing abrasions
11. Abandoning
13. In the blink of an ...
15. Scalp strands
16. Reviews (accounts)
18. Steps (on)
19. Soldier's decoration
21. Feral
22. Congers or morays

ACROSS

1. Made minor adjustments to
4. Small trumpet
7. Of the stars
8. Immerses
9. Ring of flowers
12. Letter jumbles
15. Magnificence
17. Remained
18. Parish minister
21. Weaponless
22. Unadventurous
23. Swept

DOWN

1. Tossing
2. Celestial
3. Type of herb
4. Forbids entry
5. Escape vehicle, ... car
6. Female sheep
10. Dislikes
11. Twos
13. Made unhappy
14. Eye cosmetic
16. Stroke fondly
18. Contests, ... with
19. Regretted
20. Curved hook

CROSSWORD 46

ACROSS

1. Fatal
5. Strike with foot
7. Let for rent
8. Tear violently
9. Soon, in the ... future
10. Gourd fruit
11. Skin disorder
13. At any time
14. Cheap & showy
18. Save
21. Three-piece group
22. Weak
24. White water craft
25. Motorist's fury, road ...
26. Radar screen spot
27. Common wisdom
28. This place
29. Oarsmen

DOWN

1. Greatest
2. Tree fence
3. Peruvian pack animal
4. Prior
5. Dogs' homes
6. French castle
12. Disfigure
15. Property size
16. Bishop's district
17. Gaping tiredly
19. Before (poetic)
20. Excludes
22. Less in number
23. Arm joint

ACROSS

1. Lavishly
5. Fairway sport
7. 36 inches
8. Mentally conjures up
9. Pieces of glowing coal
12. Generators
15. Topic
19. More enthusiastic
21. Detachable boat engine
22. Storybook monster
23. Thy
24. Issue (medication)

DOWN

1. Element with the symbol O
2. Confuse
3. Wicked wrongs
4. Annual
5. PNG, Papua New ...
6. Frets
10. Shapeless mass
11. Evaluate
12. Small spot
13. Facial feature
14. Principal
15. Eerie
16. Chatter wildly
17. Faint-hearted person
18. Gentle wind
19. Personal glory
20. Call up (feelings)

CROSSWORD 48

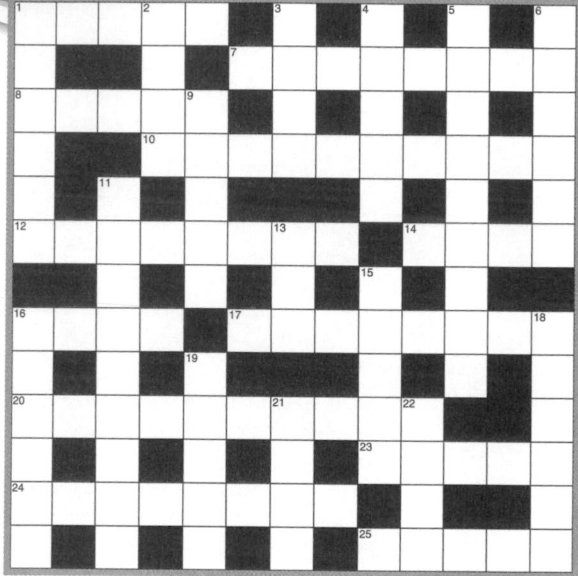

ACROSS

1. Person, ... being
7. Game fowl
8. Map within map
10. German cabbage dish
12. Piercing with knife
14. Cut with teeth
16. Be listless
17. Nice
20. Profound
23. Animal trainer
24. Most in want
25. Included

DOWN

1. Hauls up
2. Daunts
3. Clarified butter
4. Face disguises
5. Zealous
6. The ... of Liberty
9. Striped cat
11. Combat aircraft
13. No score
15. Beyond repair
16. Acting wordlessly
18. Journeyed
19. New Zealand birds
21. Talk effusively
22. Cooking fat

ACROSS

1. Of plants
4. Polluted
7. Strain
8. Talent
9. Widen (pupils)
12. Local languages
15. Proceeds (from)
17. Shouted
18. Connected to current
21. Reactor fuel
22. Dizzy
23. Thoroughly informed

DOWN

1. Apply retrospectively
2. Stadiums
3. Voucher
4. Damp & cold
5. Return bout
6. Nucleus of egg
10. Prepares (newspaper)
11. Viola flower
13. Followed closely
14. Wed
16. Shirt
18. Flight limb
19. Properly
20. Paint roughly

CROSSWORD 50

ACROSS

1. Regards smugly
5. Capricorn symbol
7. Stooped posture
8. Hornet relative
9. Spoken test
10. Owns & looks after
11. Occupy by force
13. It is, ... are
14. Automobile repair shop
18. Municipal chiefs
21. Corrosive fluid
22. Horrid
24. Kingdom
25. Square solid
26. Aviary
27. Vision
28. Egyptian cobras
29. Thread

DOWN

1. Staring rudely
2. ..., beta, gamma
3. Tremble
4. Meantime
5. Supernatural
6. Hobbyist
12. Scooped
15. Gathers
16. Postal destination
17. Trade ban
19. Assistance
20. Hang from above
22. Excludes
23. Bring upon oneself

ACROSS

1. Common cereal
7. Effortlessly
8. Aladdin's lamp servant
10. Worst behaved
12. Articles of clothing
14. Cultivate land
16. Chew
17. Unattractiveness
20. Lose speed
23. Greek oil fruit
24. Put into bondage
25. Requested, ... for

DOWN

1. Conducting (war)
2. Similar
3. Pollution haze
4. Jogs (memory)
5. Footwear manufacturer
6. Procedure
9. Painter's stand
11. Transmit
13. Yank
15. Repeat symbol
16. Small device
18. Protective screen
19. Have buoyancy
21. Shipping hazard
22. Deer

CROSSWORD 52

ACROSS

1. Commonplace
4. Regal
7. Watched over
8. Fantastic
9. Shadows (prey)
12. Celibate (relationship)
15. Re-emerge
17. Gazed fixedly
18. Thoroughfares
21. Animal hide material
22. South American parrot
23. Insect, ... mantis

DOWN

1. Major celebrity
2. Tennis score, ... fault
3. Small whirlpool
4. Birch canes
5. Barking shrilly
6. Suggestive grin
10. Espionage agents
11. Twos
13. Going sour (of milk)
14. Demonic
16. Security
18. Wander
19. Not fast
20. Elevated walkway

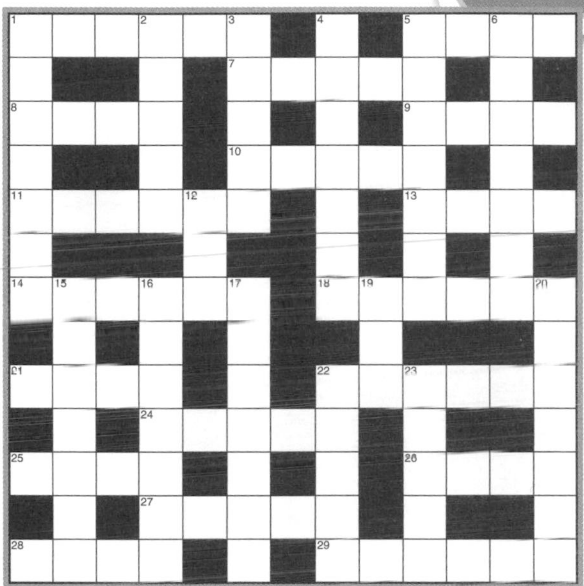

ACROSS

1. Pattern of small tiles
5. The one there
7. Lift with effort
8. Reflected sound
9. Diplomacy
10. The Press
11. Evades (capture)
13. Tidy
14. Price list
18. Recommence
21. Body fluid lump
22. Stings
24. Satellite path
25. Premonition
26. Fencing sword
27. Older of two
28. Happy
29. Up-to-date

DOWN

1. Most submissive
2. Sidestep
3. Buddies
4. Less punctual
5. Lockjaw
6. Praise
12. Folklore creature
15. Atrocious
16. Chanted
17. Outlaws
19. Deciduous tree
20. Facing the rising sun
22. Violent weather
23. Reform

CROSSWORD 54

ACROSS

1. Conrad Hilton's position
5. Forearm bone
7. Highly curious
8. Approaching
9. Garden tools
12. Dampest
15. Swiss cottages
19. Package
21. Distant settlements
22. Expended, ... up
23. Glimpse
24. Component parts

DOWN

1. Funeral vehicle
2. Bordered
3. Pop stars
4. Cooking directions
5. Extreme limit
6. Eighth month
10. District
11. Alleviate
12. They were, I ...
13. Canned fish
14. Long poem
15. Shiny metal alloy
16. Slackly
17. Delicate wrapping paper
18. Microscope plates
19. Adhesive
20. Flight path

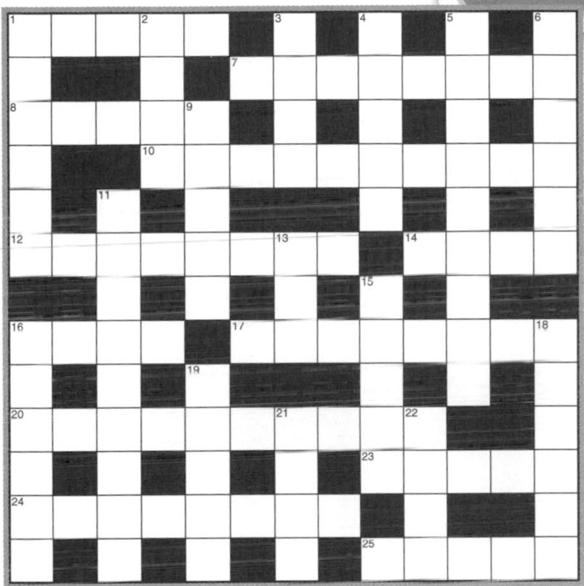

ACROSS

1. Atlantic or Pacific
7. More animated
8. Unpleasantly slippery
10. Bread snacks
12. Scolding
14. Potter's oven
16. Medication
17. Moved spasmodically
20. Attentive to detail
23. Applied levy
24. Large beer mugs
25. Serenity

DOWN

1. Pearl source
2. Goals
3. Told falsehood
4. Suit
5. Focal point
6. Penitentiary
9. Pulls with a jerk
11. Kidnapping
13. At the present moment
15. Proud walk
16. Downgrade
18. Haul up (from depths)
19. Fragment
21. Titled woman
22. Reserve

CROSSWORD 56

ACROSS

1. Law officer
4. Tests
7. Spread
8. Burn with steam
9. Began to flower
12. Assess
15. Sailing
17. Succumbs
18. Large gathering
21. Attains
22. Stroke (guitar)
23. Brief sharp pains

DOWN

1. Unspecified person
2. Subside
3. Is the right size for
4. Goes astray
5. Yearly calendar of events
6. Traded for money
10. Cotton fabric
11. Pungently tasty
13. Long letters
14. Student
16. Humiliate
18. Pros & ...
19. Small measure of spirits
20. Tense

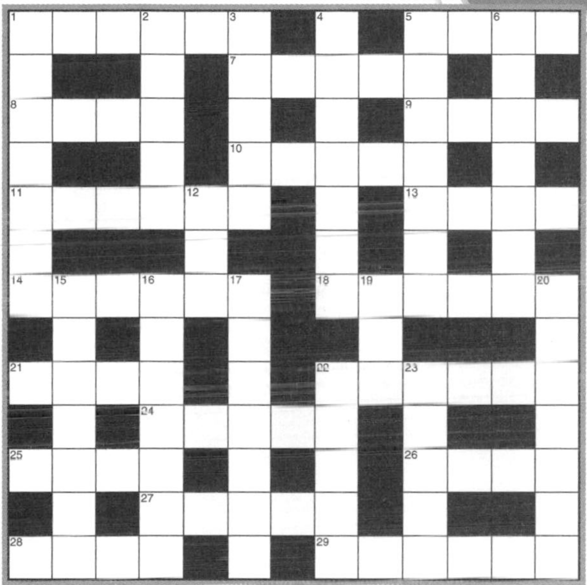

ACROSS

1. Watch out!
5. Deck mop
7. Nocturnal hours
8. Wren or jay
9. Imperial unit
10. Precipice
11. Bring from overseas
13. Jar tops
14. Doled (out)
18. Abandonment
21. Hint
22. Slid on ice
24. Coronet
25. Ancestry, family ...
26. Grizzly animal
27. Riding & roping show
28. Tints
29. Deadened

DOWN

1. Infantile
2. Of sound
3. Put into effect
4. Set fire to
5. Represses
6. Shopping walkways
12. Caviar
15. Sensitivity to substance
16. Weight watchers
17. Insists on
19. Annoy
20. Suffered
22. Beauty establishment
23. Stamp book

CROSSWORD 58

ACROSS

1. Sang in unison
5. Tiny amount
7. Small island
8. Faintest
9. Camera glasses
12. Jury finding
15. Most pious
19. Annul
21. Kept steady
22. Freezes, ... over
23. Ore seam
24. Esteems

DOWN

1. Cools
2. Smells strongly
3. Open wounds
4. Injure
5. Mean
6. Painter
10. Not binding
11. Otherwise, or ...
12. Critically examine
13. Talk excitedly
14. Novel thought
15. Of medicinal plants
16. Inherited
17. UFO, flying ...
18. Tightens (muscles)
19. Plant stem lumps
20. False appearance

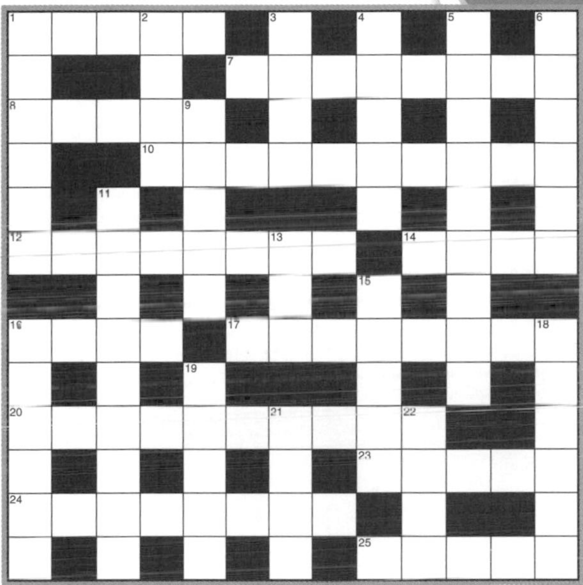

ACROSS

1. Suspect's excuse
7. Flight industry
8. Skewered dish
10. Sleepy feeling
12. Ocean voyager
14. Wheedle
16. Actor, ... Sharif
17. Calmly
20. Counterfeit
23. Song of the Swiss
24. Sketching carbon
25. Bequeath

DOWN

1. Lower leg joints
2. Necklace component
3. Affirm
4. Paved terrace
5. Missile's strength
6. For men or women
9. Snap
11. Twin hulled boat
13. Supplement, ... out
15. Wet (weather)
16. Place of business
18. Daffodil hue
19. Authoritative command
21. Lend to
22. Urban community

CROSSWORD 60

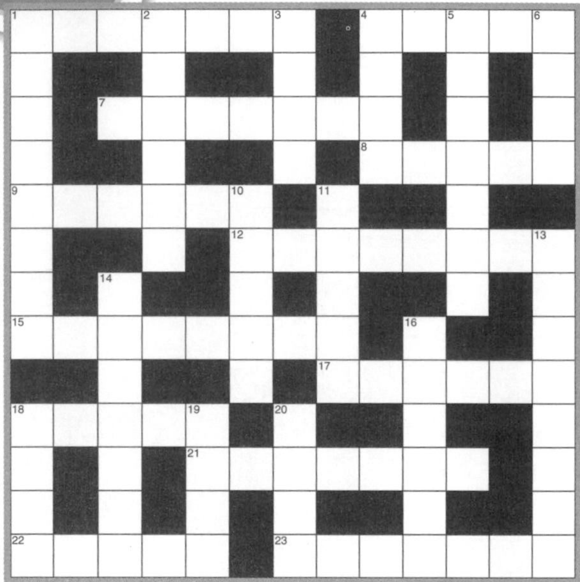

ACROSS

1. Chinese river
4. Hollow
7. Least attractive
8. Declare
9. Small celestial body
12. Speeches
15. People taken from danger
17. Cured
18. Cite author
21. Acted in response
22. Defined regions
23. Gloomier

DOWN

1. Californian national park
2. Choked
3. Equal
4. Consumes food
5. Self-contradiction
6. Ox harness
10. Actor's parts
11. Grating
13. Poorer quality
14. Wool fat
16. Photographer's tool
18. Trivia test
19. Periods of time
20. Door frame post

ACROSS

1. Puzzle
5. Wharf
7. Spree
8. Inheritor
9. Bread portion
10. Not explicit
11. Film star dog
13. Serving platter
14. Join in half-heartedly
18. Ran rapidly
21. Printing fluids
22. Afraid
24. Remove completely
25. Grant
26. Injure with horns
27. Recurrent period
28. Legend
29. Torrid

DOWN

1. Expelled air
2. Disease agents
3. Higher than
4. Caught on barb
5. Crosses out
6. Mime
12. Sick
15. Yearly stipend
16. Implore
17. Increase in attractiveness
19. Rainbow shape
20. Frail with age
22. Genders
23. Debate

CROSSWORD 62

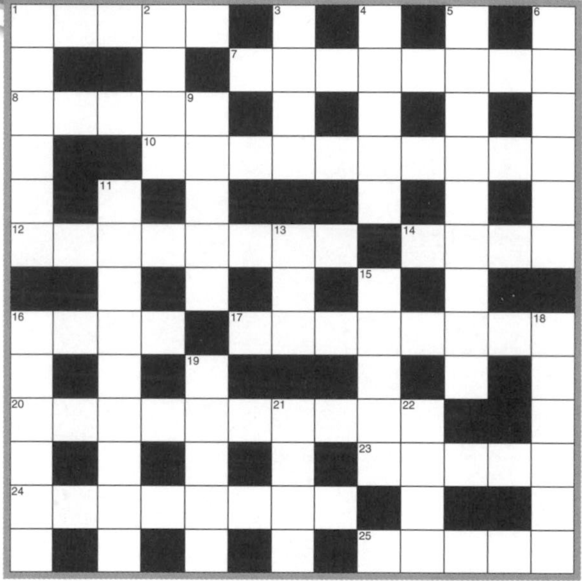

ACROSS

1. Privileged class
7. Former soldiers
8. Edible organs
10. Horseracing track
12. Entitling
14. Done breaststroke
16. Tasks
17. Scraps
20. Pop instrumentalists
23. Finnish steam bath
24. Highly charged
25. River-mouth land

DOWN

1. Develop
2. Rupture
3. Measure (out)
4. Furnishing scheme
5. Diminishing
6. Admiration
9. Large spoon
11. Partly cooked
13. Gesture of assent
15. Radiates
16. Sharply serrated
18. Musical composition
19. Taunts
21. Curved-bill bird
22. Auction

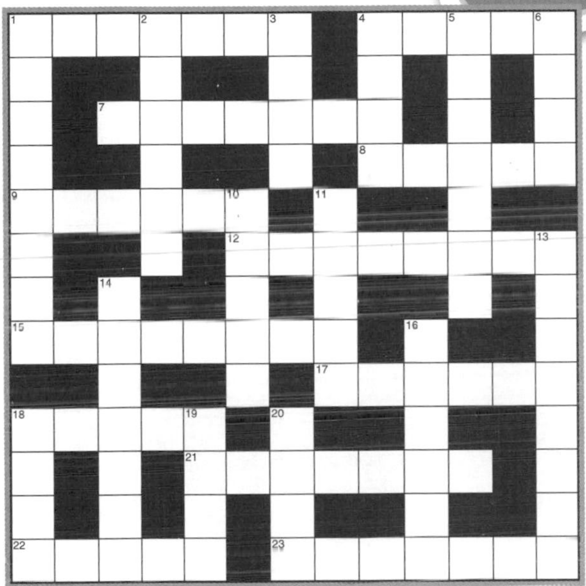

ACROSS

1. True
4. Pituitary or adrenal
7. Stowing space
8. Accurate
9. Me, ... & I
12. Surprised, taken ...
15. Cadets
17. Prohibited narcotic
18. Breakfasts or dinners
21. Climatic conditions
22. Intended
23. Clung (to)

DOWN

1. Most important
2. Captioned
3. Slope
4. Mirth
5. News & current ...
6. Grime
10. Welded
11. Swamp
13. Average
14. Card game
16. Light wind
18. Incapacitate
19. Squash (insect)
20. Festival

CROSSWORD 64

ACROSS

1. Wily
5. Pen tips
7. Lead-in
8. Brave man
9. On an occasion
10. Lazed
11. Have effect (on)
13. Scalp parasites
14. Oversee
18. Dress ribbons
21. Tropical tree
22. More profound
24. Irritating to the skin
25. Terrace level
26. Cattle prod
27. Run off to marry
28. Old
29. Becomes faster, ... up

DOWN

1. Religious non-belief
2. Local vegetation
3. Extent
4. Sloping typeface
5. Asian food items
6. Tour de France vehicle
12. Wheel tooth
15. Astounding
16. Respected
17. Pilot safety aid, ... seat
19. Beer
20. Long steps
22. Dutch sea walls
23. Golfer's two under par

ACROSS

1. Most agile
5. Peel
7. Uncouth
8. Walked
9. Go by (of time)
12. Aspiring actress
15. River of ice
19. Grills
21. Wired message
22. Salute
23. Went on horseback
24. Hearing membranes

DOWN

1. Hospital workers
2. Paging device sound
3. Follow next
4. Front of neck
5. Big dipper, ... coaster
6. Subtract
10. Vocal solo
11. Sri Lankan robe
12. Male title
13. Type of saxophone
14. Large amounts
15. Roadside channel
16. Dairy product
17. Come into view
18. Biblical prayers
19. More docile
20. Dislike intensely

CROSSWORD 66

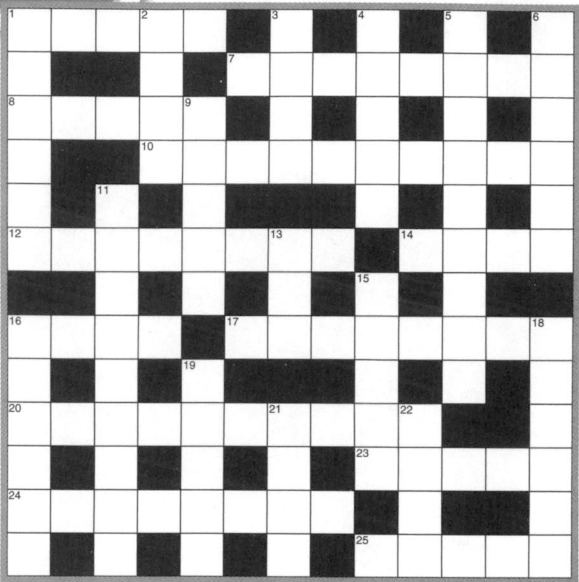

ACROSS

1. Desert wanderer
7. Scandal
8. Cape
10. Logically
12. Bluffing
14. Unit of land
16. Grassed section
17. Canines
20. Unwillingness
23. Inuit canoe
24. Provoking
25. Group of musical notes

DOWN

1. Rock face recesses
2. A great distance
3. New Zealand bird
4. Acute pain
5. Bolted (of gate)
6. Rewrite on keyboard
9. Buddhist fate
11. Careless pedestrian
13. Opposite of aye
15. Protruded, ... out
16. Tempting
18. Chopped wildly
19. Rough-skinned
21. Female relative
22. Apiece

ACROSS

1. Found
4. Ahead of time
7. Stir
8. Speak slowly
9. Stared angrily
12. Most immature
15. Divergent lines
17. Emotional shock
18. Torment
21. Technical sketch
22. Literary style
23. Perspired

DOWN

1. Lawsuit contestant
2. Enrages
3. Tie in race
4. Viewed
5. Delighted
6. Shout
10. Perishing
11. Erupted
13. Foiled
14. Untouched (of meal)
16. Curved fruit
18. Tiny branch
19. Rim
20. Flying mammals

CROSSWORD 68

ACROSS

1. Precious metal
5. Yacht
7. Public persona
8. Enthusiastic devotion
9. Citrus tree
10. Tropical fruit
11. Mauve flowers
13. Drew
14. Stupefying
18. Military students
21. Uterus
22. Made airtight
24. Awkward
25. Clothing
26. Fencing sword
27. Fill with joy
28. Baron's title
29. Sprites

DOWN

1. Fried noisily
2. Italian country house
3. Circles
4. Extremist
5. Tardy
6. Side of chair
12. Tin container
15. Guacamole ingredient
16. Partook of alcohol
17. Entrance
19. Gorilla or chimpanzee
20. Jockeys' seats
22. Sheer
23. Fasten (to)

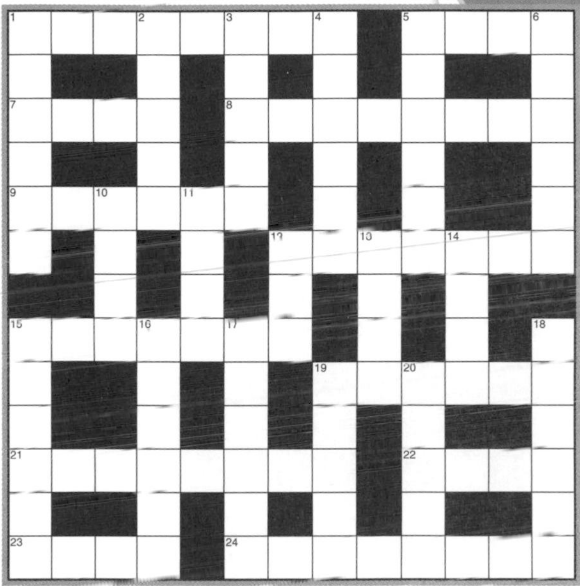

ACROSS

1. Retaliation
5. Sentence component
7. Metal join
8. Bread shops
9. Steering device
12. Scent
15. Wash
19. Noisy confusion
21. Regarding smugly
22. Undercooked (steak)
23. Eat
24. Rubber overshoes

DOWN

1. Money for good deed
2. Remade
3. Unaffected by alcohol
4. Points out similarity
5. Trill
6. Prescribed amount
10. Desert hill
11. Gain
12. Lamb's mother
13. Equivalent
14. Carpentry spike
15. Obtained by begging
16. Wear away
17. Witnessing
18. Lodges firmly
19. Ring-shaped bun
20. Mends with needle

CROSSWORD 70

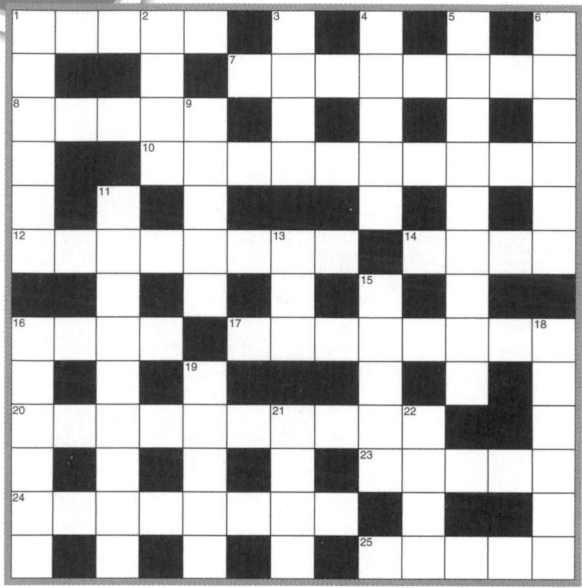

ACROSS

1. Show to be true
7. Missing person's tracker
8. Lethal
10. Washing (clothes)
12. Prevented entry of
14. Slide
16. Annual period
17. Got
20. Nobleman
23. Nominated
24. Unnecessary
25. Not as good

DOWN

1. Swollen, ... up
2. Calf meat
3. Actor, ... Penn
4. Wept
5. Screeching
6. Very cold
9. Animal dens
11. Polishing substances
13. Flow away
15. Infidel
16. Pines (for)
18. Lag behind
19. Stable compartment
21. Travel bag
22. Mexican snack

ACROSS

1. Forceful
4. Shirtsleeve edges
7. Cats
8. Stockpile
9. Accommodated
12. Occasion
15. Release
17. Laundry stiffener
18. Assisted
21. Citrus crop
22. Cherub
23. Tied (laces)

DOWN

1. Away from summit
2. Opposed
3. Sugar source
4. Money
5. Scavenges
6. Beach material
10. Female opera singers
11. Dull pains
13. Hitched
14. Tolerating
16. Lying dormant
18. Spiritual glow
19. Girl's plaything
20. Songbird

CROSSWORD 72

ACROSS

1. Overdue (bill)
5. Tree part
7. Hostile opponent
8. Crustacean with nippers
9. Captures (criminal)
10. Uniform
11. Accessories
13. Wig material
14. Disorderly crowd
18. Quit
21. Heavily promote
22. Held responsible
24. Illustrious
25. Discover
26. Delivery vehicles
27. Wear away
28. Act
29. Long claws

DOWN

1. Obscure
2. Fossil resin
3. Concave impressions
4. Wander
5. Hangs unlawfully
6. Walking slowly
12. Trouble
15. Whenever
16. Mixed
17. Arch over eye
19. Snake-like fish
20. Naturists
22. Besieged
23. Blacksmith's block

ACROSS

1. Unstable (of chemical)
5. Object of worship
7. Towards interior of
8. Straw-roofed (cottage)
9. Commander
12. Sheep pelts
15. Revised
19. Genetically copied
21. Leaving empty
22. Govern
23. Actor, ... Nolte
24. Accentuates

DOWN

1. Futilely
2. Audibly
3. Place in crypt
4. Tooth covering
5. Earnings
6. Ski chalets
10. Amongst
11. Prepare (newspaper)
12. Short-lived trend
13. Wicked
14. Maize
15. Irregular
16. Go on offensive
17. Covets
18. Vipers
19. Tobacco product
20. Giant monsters

CROSSWORD 74

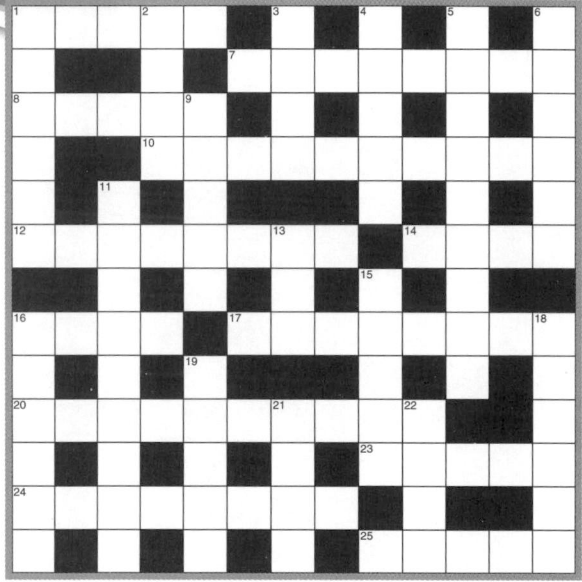

ACROSS

1. Massage
7. Escapes
8. Fantasy
10. Sixtieth, ..., eightieth
12. Protest posters
14. Roman gown
16. Area round teeth
17. Chemical building block
20. Wicked
23. Placed
24. Brightness
25. Glided on snow

DOWN

1. Abduct
2. Regrettably
3. Double-reed instrument
4. Severe (illness)
5. Lack of propriety
6. Breathing disorder
9. Tin or lead
11. Citrus preserve
13. Musical twosome
15. Bills of fare
16. Rule (country)
18. Eluded (capture)
19. Tokyo is there
21. Narrow part of bottle
22. Unwell

ACROSS

1. Pulling sharply
4. Stretch (for)
7. Hungarian spice
8. Tennis score
9. Risk
12. Rescued disaster victims
15. Gaining knowledge
17. Radio interference
18. Roves
21. Tetanus ailment
22. Stacked
23. Monotony

DOWN

1. Young in appearance
2. Australian marsupials
3. Clench (teeth)
4. Street
5. Adopts (identity)
6. Fine-tune (skills)
10. Cotton fabric
11. Sudden pains
13. Rainbow's band of hues
14. Sun shield
16. Japanese martial art
18. Hindquarters
19. Sleigh
20. Sore crust

CROSSWORD 76

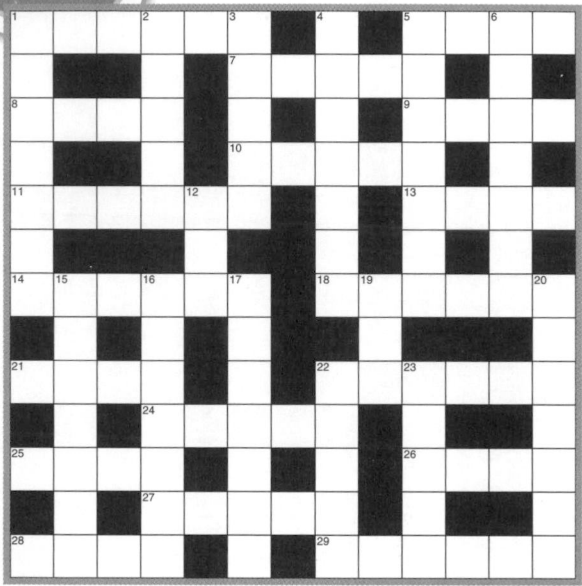

ACROSS

1. Amusingly coarse
5. Castle water ditch
7. Senseless (comment)
8. Hawaiian dance
9. Grumble
10. Dining bench
11. Cows' milk sacs
13. Not one
14. More effortless
18. Phantoms
21. Collar button
22. Wellbeing
24. Female reproductive organ
25. Forbid
26. Injury
27. Ascended
28. Operates
29. Records

DOWN

1. Reaccommodate
2. Conscious
3. Slimming plans
4. Poking abruptly
5. Token of remembrance
6. Opposed to
12. Regret
15. National songs
16. Within building
17. Fall ill again
19. Garden tool
20. Plots
22. African scavenger
23. Pallid

ACROSS

1. Connective tissue
5. Tired sigh
7. Brass Instrument
8. Pennant mast
9. Parentless child
12. Peruses
15. Common analgesic
19. Together, in ...
21. Bent down
22. Gone away
23. Transmit
24. Banned sports drugs

DOWN

1. Cosmetic fluid
2. Flooded by waves
3. Pixie-like
4. Leaf beverage pourer
5. Barked shrilly
6. Sister's daughters
10. Furtive glance
11. Half-open
12. Solar body
13. Atop
14. Charged atoms
15. Chinese calculating frame
16. Distributed
17. Linear units
18. Joins
19. Excessive
20. Snow shelter

CROSSWORD 78

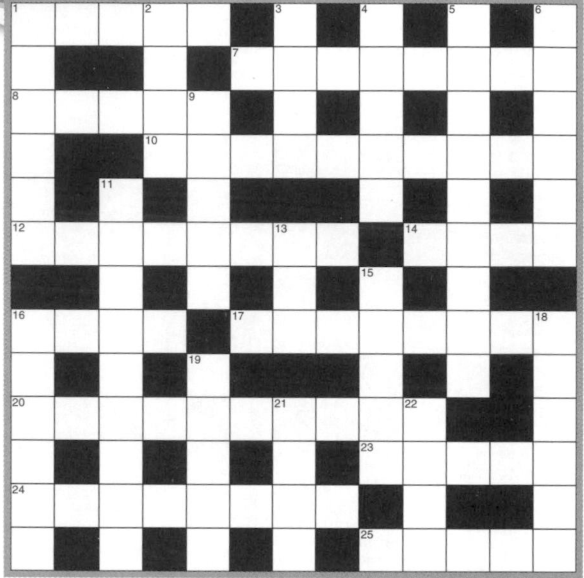

ACROSS

1. Rapid
7. Likely
8. Trample
10. Jingling percussion instrument
12. Relieve of anxieties
14. Piebald
16. Young lions
17. Hand-clapping
20. Pirates
23. Italian dish
24. Personal reminiscence
25. Rap

DOWN

1. Artist's model
2. Brave deed
3. Infant's bed
4. Concerning
5. Unaware
6. Decapitate
9. Common flower
11. Cooked outdoors
13. Dangerous sea current
15. Suck noisily
16. Venomous hooded snakes
18. Set off
19. Comes to earth
21. Feeds on
22. Hewn (logs)

ACROSS

1. Male spouse
4. Allude
7. Mainly
8. Room
9. Flung
12. Improper
15. Seizing
17. Executes (law)
18. Looks longingly
21. Tires
22. Child's toy, ... bear
23. Endless

DOWN

1. Emerging from egg
2. For, on ... of
3. Resist
4. Sunbeams
5. Had buoyancy
6. Lariat
10. Finger or toe
11. Wise saying
13. Unsuspecting
14. Blinded by light
16. Profession
18. Central idea
19. Move to & fro
20. Celebrity status

CROSSWORD 80

ACROSS

1. Vicious
5. Increased in size
7. Prepared
8. Turn over
9. Paper quantity
10. Shopping mall
11. Draw forth
13. Udder tip
14. Bicycle for two
18. Blush
21. Yoked beasts
22. South American parrots
24. Absurd
25. Burrowing mammal
26. No longer here
27. Return (of symptoms)
28. Invites
29. Type of wasp

DOWN

1. Quietest
2. Meat jelly
3. Burst
4. Spanish bullfighter
5. Rotated
6. Originate
12. Chill
15. Nervously tense
16. Ballerinas
17. King or queen
19. Chapter in history
20. Most inquisitive
22. Incense resin
23. Large roll of tobacco

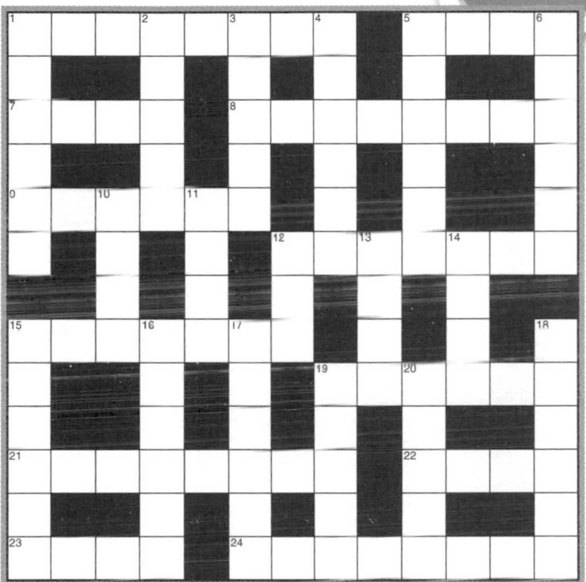

ACROSS

1. Introductory statement
5. Eccentric
7. Remove wrapping from
8. Used logic
9. Overwhelm by sound
12. Rocking cribs
15. Fishing vessel
19. Wetlands
21. Pulled a face
22. Loud laugh
23. Blacken by fire
24. Unexpectedly

DOWN

1. UK currency units
2. Icily detached
3. Media tycoon, press ...
4. Pencil-mark remover
5. Used close-up lens
6. Sings alpine-style
10. Region
11. Sinister
12. Train carriage
13. Over again
14. Weaving apparatus
15. Terribly sad
16. Hotter
17. Votes for
18. Off course
19. Teamed (with)
20. Consent

CROSSWORD 82

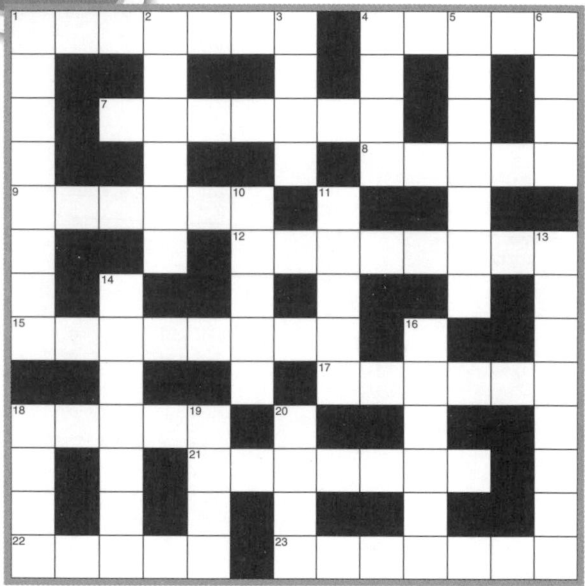

ACROSS

1. Spoke indistinctly
4. Visits, ... on
7. Clear gemstone
8. Glorify
9. Lyrics
12. Regretted
15. Instances
17. Allow
18. Book of maps
21. Net-dragging vessel
22. Adversary
23. Frenzied

DOWN

1. Impel
2. Of weddings
3. Dire fate
4. Give up (territory)
5. Faithfulness
6. Opening for coin
10. Cunningly
11. Cause laughter
13. Of the home
14. Transport of goods
16. Cave chamber
18. Actress, ... Hathaway
19. Remain
20. Fifty per cent

ACROSS

1. Desert illusion
5. Wound with dagger
7. Adjudicator
8. Confiscate
9. Male fowl
10. Seat
11. Shocked
13. Give off
14. Decrees
18. Lessening
21. Tinted
22. Colloquial sayings
24. Protect
25. Foundation
26. Travel cost
27. Shelf
28. Belonging to that girl
29. Ambulance warnings

DOWN

1. Natural gas
2. Sports ground
3. Oust
4. Move forward
5. Confidential matters
6. Sale by bids
12. Perched
15. Eddie Murphy comedy, Daddy ... (3,3)
16. Truncheons
17. Threads
19. As well
20. Sealants
22. Lazes
23. Deduce

CROSSWORD 84

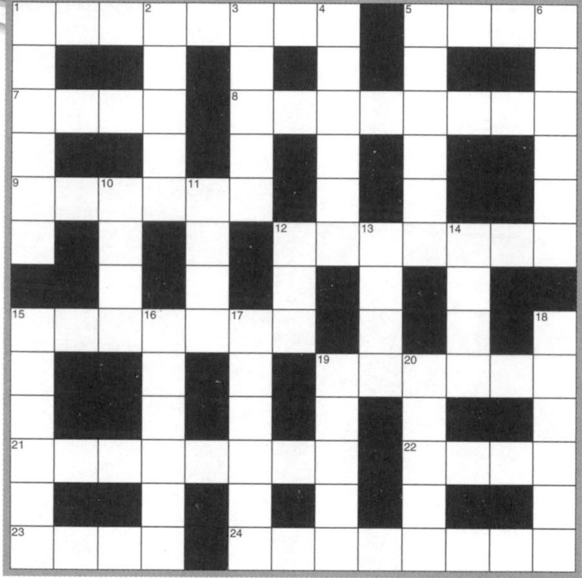

ACROSS

1. Brews
5. Tibetan priest
7. Volcanic flow
8. Leaping over
9. Swiss cottage
12. Played the lead
15. Suspended
19. Spurn
21. Giving therapy to
22. Face covering
23. Shoe cord
24. Architectural overhaul

DOWN

1. Unbleached cotton
2. Move on hands & knees
3. Envy
4. Eject (liquid)
5. Pig's young
6. Sharply bent
10. Yemeni port
11. Wicked
12. Sorrowful
13. Competent
14. Fragrant flower
15. Of teeth
16. Lubricate
17. Weirder
18. Taken by thief
19. Went on rampage
20. Dances to rock & roll

ACROSS

1. Dog parasites
7. Monuments seen from the Nile
8. Ox stomach
10. Improve the flow of
12. Pragmatists
14. Huge
16. Drama
17. Fiddled with thumbs
20. Comic portrait
23. Remove errors from
24. Impertinent
25. Composition

DOWN

1. Male parent
2. Swiss mountains
3. Variety
4. Incapacitates
5. Likewise
6. Upward climb
9. Moral standard
11. Section of writing
13. Pull by rope
15. Love deeply
16. Outdoor meal
18. Lethal
19. Corrosive fluids
21. Army vehicle
22. Ostrich-like birds

CROSSWORD 86

ACROSS

1. Unpredictable
4. Thin candle
7. Layer
8. Oval nut
9. Romancing
12. Slaughterhouse
15. Cease developing
17. Hung in folds
18. Outside limits
21. Angrily
22. Narrow elevation
23. Fatigue

DOWN

1. Gives authority to
2. Gain
3. Lions & tigers
4. Short-term worker
5. South American cloaks
6. Riding strap
10. Carnivals
11. Sped
13. Noisiest
14. Rinsed throat
16. Mexican flower
18. Large pitcher
19. Extent
20. Front of head

ACROSS

1. Tropical lizard
5. Footwear item
7. Put
8. Noisy
9. Slightly open
10. Australian gems
11. Cardboard box
13. Electrical resistance units
14. Inborn skill
18. Wish
21. Pigs
22. Surgeon
24. Under no circumstances
25. Temporary visitor document
26. Bowl
27. Infuriates
28. Sandal or boot
29. Saturated

DOWN

1. Illegal
2. Accounts check
3. Kitchen smock
4. Marched
5. Summer & winter
6. Beguiling person
12. Possess
15. Eliminate
16. Entrap
17. Journeys
19. Self-image
20. Made from clay
22. Frock
23. Encrypted

CROSSWORD 88

ACROSS

1. Proffered
5. Jest
7. A long time
8. Remarkable events
9. Refreshment stands
12. Pursued stealthily
15. Bewildered
19. Sponged
21. Swiftest
22. Open mouth wide
23. Poultry products
24. Calming drug

DOWN

1. Appreciation
2. Brushes (off)
3. Cavorts
4. Straight
5. Wild African canine
6. Eventuated
10. Was obliged to pay
11. Ship's spine
12. Lump of turf
13. Water
14. Door handle
15. Muslim temple
16. Dance nightclubs
17. Painters' tripods
18. Stick (to)
19. Loved excessively, ... on
20. Prejudiced person

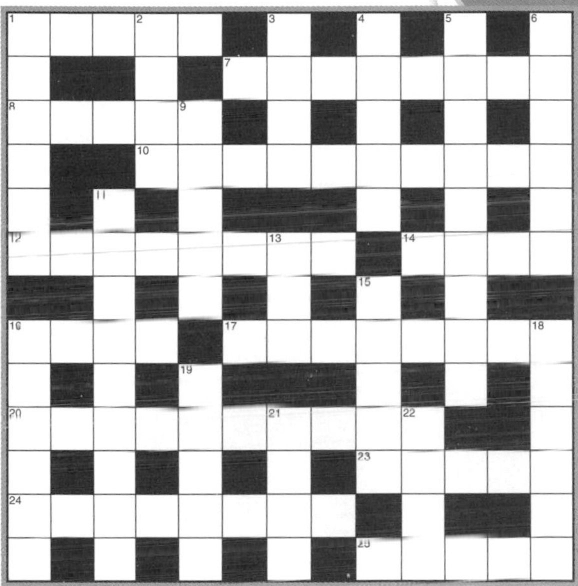

ACROSS

1. Performed
7. Clamber
8. Either yes or no
10. Strolling
12. Put at risk
14. Leer
16. Loading wharf
17. Decreed
20. Came (from)
23. Nude
24. Furthest limits
25. Malice

DOWN

1. Respect
2. Flows away
3. Computer symbol
4. Palm fruits
5. Condensing
6. Jamaican music
9. Deserves
11. Perfectionists
13. Misjudge
15. Sanctuary
16. Speech extracts
18. Absent-minded scribble
19. Bee homes
21. Discontinued (project)
22. Moist

CROSSWORD 90

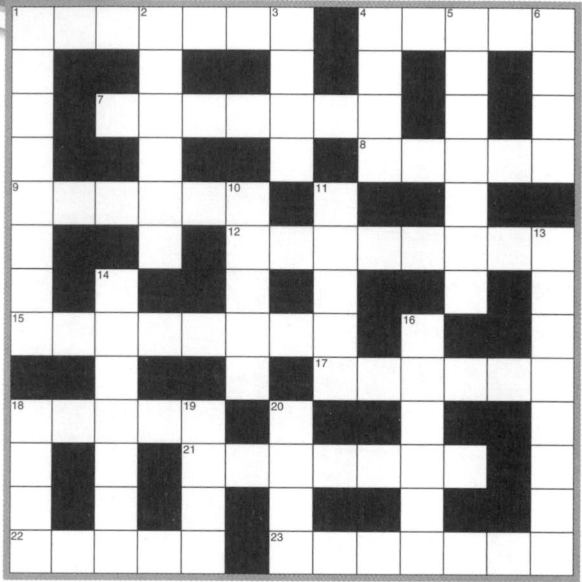

ACROSS

1. Nearby
4. Tremble
7. Predicament
8. Ups & ...
9. Expressions of pain
12. Beseeched
15. Small grains
17. Nastier
18. Duck's call
21. Envision
22. Stage of development
23. Fruit tree grove

DOWN

1. Reclining casually
2. Zoo inmate
3. Tropical root vegetables
4. Rectangular courtyard
5. Uncomfortable (situation)
6. Scrapes by, ... out a living
10. Stupid
11. Twitch
13. Undressed
14. Mosquito-borne fever
16. Middle-age spread
18. Wisecrack
19. Flying toy
20. Ballroom dance, ... doble

ACROSS

1. Made cat sound
5. Pounce
7. Sad poem
8. Arm or leg
9. Pleasant
10. Ancient remnant
11. Anomaly
13. Owl's cry
14. Brutal
18. Unassuming
21. Spur
22. Complied with
24. Become informed
25. Very short skirt
26. Tablet
27. Light push
28. Male red deer
29. Rudder handle

DOWN

1. Bed headrests
2. Jewish scholar
3. Denounce
4. Recover (goods)
5. Hanged unlawfully
6. Mooring weights
12. Price ticket
15. Rescue by helicopter
16. Confounding
17. Enlarges
19. Globe
20. Walking infant
22. Beginning
23. Throw out

CROSSWORD 92

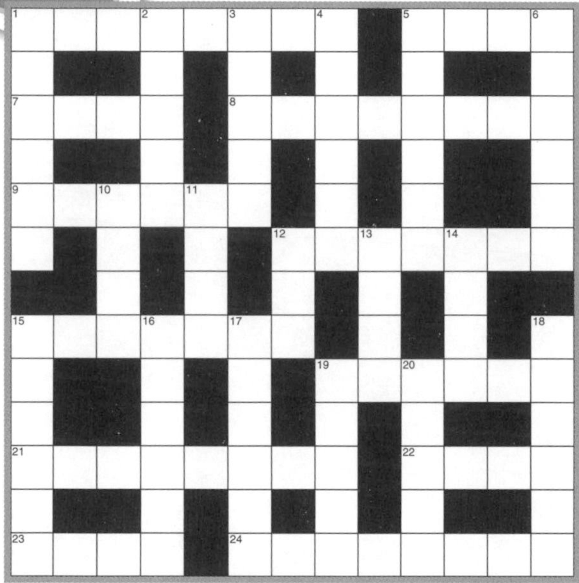

ACROSS

1. To the point
5. Expired
7. Large tooth
8. Questioner
9. Ogled, ... at
12. Referee's device
15. Line of hereditary rulers
19. Burglaries
21. Financial
22. Stupor
23. Decoy
24. Makes stable

DOWN

1. Sweepstake
2. Enthusiastic
3. In front
4. Roofing grass
5. Floats on current
6. Ridicule
10. Uniform
11. Grain tips
12. Route
13. Skin irritation
14. Slight quarrel
15. Gloomy
16. For each one
17. Sums
18. Evaluate
19. Cooking herb
20. Terminated

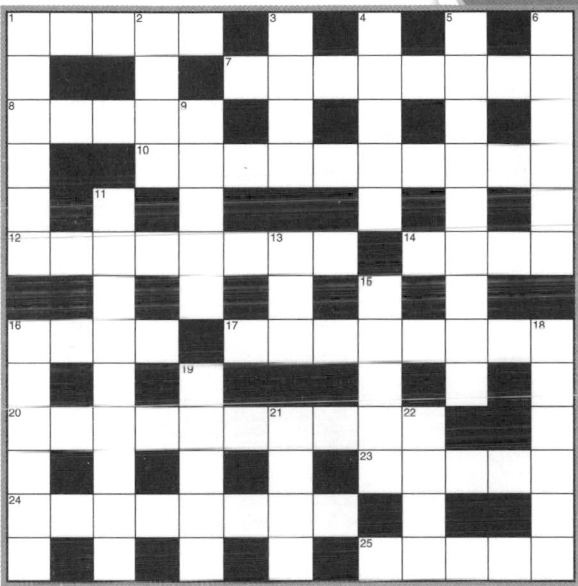

ACROSS

1. Inquiry
7. Emotional eruption
8. Lowest female voices
10. Moderation
12. Disgraces
14. Be sullen
16. Resign
17. Clearly expressed
20. Overstate
23. Brown pigment
24. Cosmetic pencil
25. UK & Eire, The British ...

DOWN

1. Fluid units
2. Unruly protest
3. Refuse heap
4. Terminate
5. Say correct way
6. Flash (of lightning)
9. Dingy
11. Drools
13. Negligent
15. Darts
16. Waits in line
18. Pinches (nose)
19. Once more
21. Fishing spool
22. Morays

CROSSWORD 94

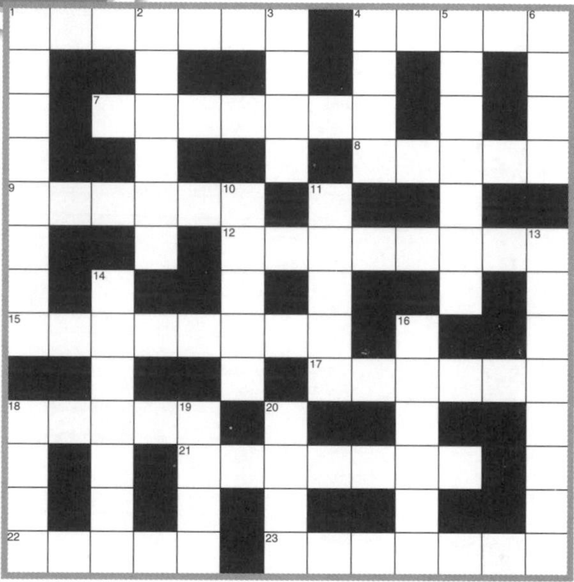

ACROSS

1. Worn by friction
4. Plucked string sound
7. Old-fashioned
8. Playing-card Jack
9. Wallop
12. Runaways
15. Scriptwriter's words
17. Combined forces, ... up
18. Give lessons
21. Saying yes to
22. This 24 hours
23. Carve

DOWN

1. Confessed
2. Aviator
3. Twofold
4. Garment fold
5. Assumed identities
6. Heredity unit
10. Shrub fence
11. Eight-piece group
13. Set of symptoms
14. Quit (premises)
16. Mode
18. Clump of grass
19. Hallowed
20. Disabled

ACROSS

1. Spanish fleet
5. Draw in (air)
7. Stale
8. Dingy
9. In the area of
10. Volley of bullets
11. Crowd brawls
13. Have (to)
14. Caught in the act
18. Entangle
21. Unnatural sleep
22. Library user
24. Actress, ... Kelly
25. Bully
26. Take nap
27. Happening
28. Electricity supply network
29. Moves furtively

DOWN

1. Stomach
2. Leisurely walk
3. Accumulate
4. Set apart
5. Like-meaning word
6. Meteor impact holes
12. Before (poetic)
15. One good turn deserves ...
16. Crowed
17. Formal arguments
19. Maiden name indicator
20. Horse restrainer
22. Hires out
23. Contributed

CROSSWORD 96

ACROSS

1. Absconders
5. Always
7. Tiny branch
8. Not scared
9. Dehydration symptom
12. Plods
15. Vulgar
19. More orderly
21. Very distressing
22. Loan
23. Light sleeps
24. Laterally

DOWN

1. Gyrate
2. Hostility
3. Mature
4. Beard trimmer
5. Fetching task
6. FM receivers
10. Woes
11. Confident
12. Musical, ... Wizard Of Oz
13. Encourage
14. Squall
15. Life gas
16. Desert animals
17. Sheer hosiery
18. Wears away
19. Nuzzled
20. Let

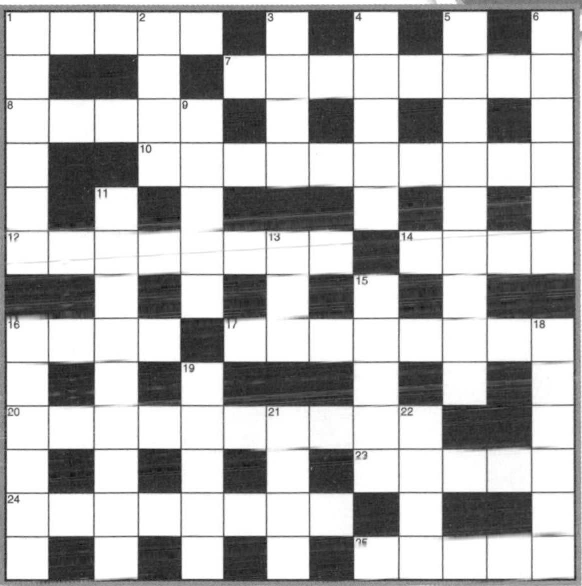

ACROSS

1. Balanced
7. Game fowl
8. Rebuke
10. Blessed
12. Chewing
14. Office circular
16. Extended family
17. Protested
20. Pillaging
23. Crave, ... for
24. Tarried
25. Sham

DOWN

1. Naval flag
2. Suffers
3. Stylish
4. Sweet herb
5. Political declaration
6. Recording room
9. Dawdle
11. Getting
13. End of pen
15. Beatles hit, ... Lane
16. Christmas songs
18. Mended with needle
19. Spent time idly
21. Leg joint
22. Equipment

CROSSWORD 98

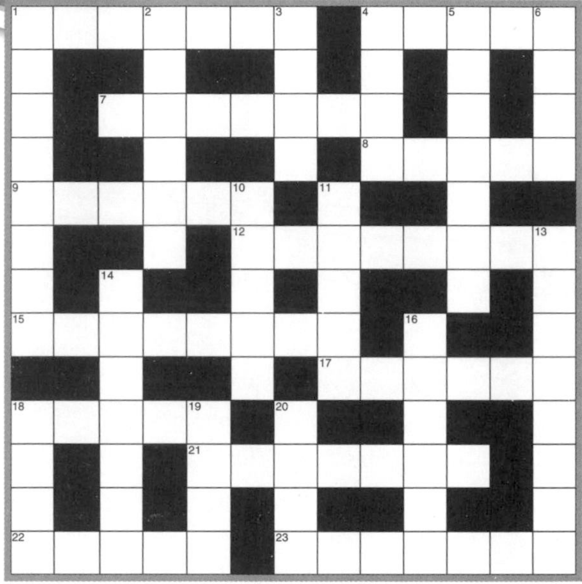

ACROSS

1. Pursuing closely
4. Hollywood prize, Academy ...
7. Grove of fruit trees
8. You will, we ...
9. Glows
12. Strolls aimlessly
15. Collar
17. Cried in pain
18. Burglary warning
21. Word jumble
22. Edition
23. Young hare

DOWN

1. Snow sled
2. Lasso
3. Desired result
4. Support devices
5. Displayed
6. Unexciting
10. Spread
11. Rice field
13. Leafiest
14. Scratches (surface)
16. Gratify
18. Opposed to
19. Confusing network
20. Trip over

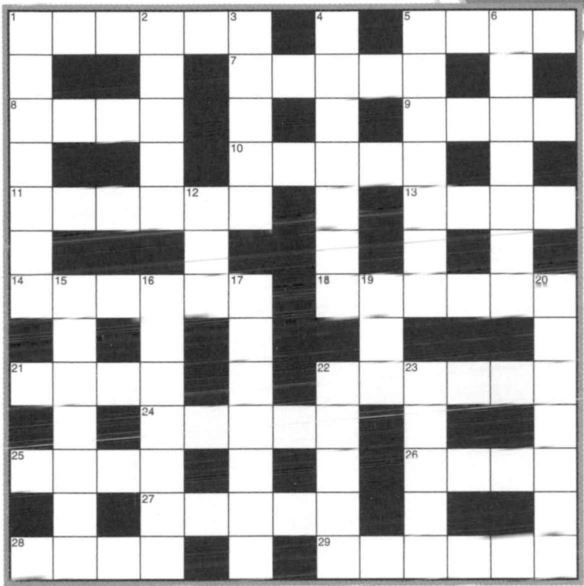

ACROSS

1. Detect
6. Prods sharply
7. Exaggeratedly masculine
8. Defined region
9. Seepage
10. Shine
11. Bee's liquid harvest
13. Single object
14. Carnivores, meat ...
18. Most painful
21. Cougar
22. Stood on hind legs
24. Terminate
25. Days of yore, the ...
26. Graceful bird
27. Clear
28. Refuse to admit
29. Wool clippers

DOWN

1. Throat capsule
2. Adroit
3. Piece of glowing coal
4. Frozen water spikes
5. Merrier
6. Sportsmen's jackets
12. Ventilate
15. Flatter to excess
16. Precisely
17. Graze
19. Primary number
20. News
22. Splits apart
23. Supermarket lane

ACROSS

1. Comes undone
5. Doing word
7. Feral
8. Envy
9. Brawl
12. Movie inspectors
15. Inflated ball
19. Tenderly
21. Rigidity
22. Plaintive howl
23. Fades
24. Obliterates

DOWN

1. Remove cover from
2. Snake, puff ...
3. Like
4. Scant
5. Pansies
6. Purchasers
10. Duck or chicken
11. Too
12. Cheat
13. Memorandum
14. Leave out
15. Polished
16. Peru beasts
17. Displease
18. Recurrent periods
19. Fights for air
20. Fresher

ACROSS

1. Opposite of rural
7. Daughter's child
8. Common
10. Juveniles
12. Complete disorder
14. Rushed
16. Glass pots
17. Looking very undernourished
20. Significant
23. Brought under control
24. Most fortunate
25. Sense of the absurd

DOWN

1. Dethrones
2. Not here
3. Wide smile
4. Grind (teeth) together
5. Bone specialist
6. Unexpended
9. Hotel foyer
11. Male family head
13. Large deer
15. Disobey (rules)
16. Mixture
18. Indecently
19. Inflexible
21. Deep wound
22. Den

CROSSWORD 102

ACROSS

1. Nutrient (pill)
4. End of war
7. Nervously restless
8. Wrap for head & shoulders
9. Remained
12. Leaves (sinking ship)
15. Regional speeches
17. Greatly pleased
18. Complete
21. Of the beach
22. Family adage
23. Deserved

DOWN

1. Disappeared
2. Every time
3. Actor, ... Nolte
4. Settles account
5. Pilot
6. Fragrant type of tea, ... Grey
10. Move to music
11. Make happen
13. Followed secretly
14. Lowest British titled rank
16. Italian sausage
18. To ... it may concern
19. Resound
20. Pacify

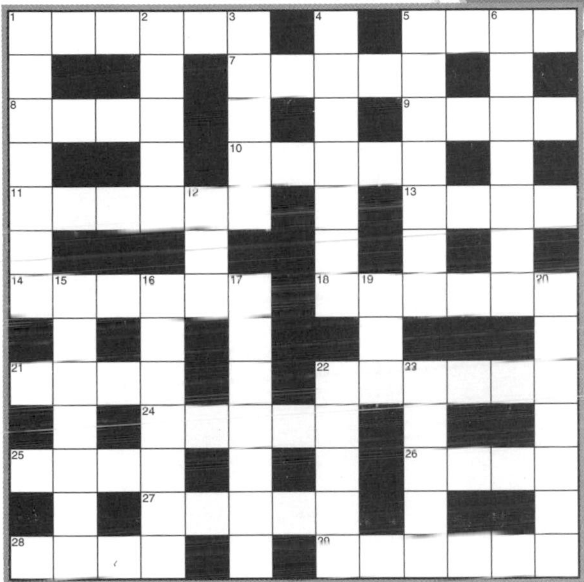

ACROSS

1. Recoil
5. Unbiased
7. Mindful
8. Absconded
9. Rework
10. Braid
11. Eradicates
13. In a casual way
14. Inform
18. Slimmed
21. Consumer
22. Exemplify
24. Weight unit
25. Asian sauce bean
26. Vehicle for hire
27. Ate out
28. Tennis court barriers
29. Globe

DOWN

1. Quarter of an hour, ... minutes
2. Naked models
3. Stringed instruments
4. Injured
5. Rich (soil)
6. Luxuriate
12. Sprite
15. Blowing from sea
16. Encroachments
17. Gaping
19. Creeping plant
20. Dawn to dusk
22. Is inclined (to)
23. Slope of roof

CROSSWORD 104

ACROSS

1. Roman M
5. Part of fish-hook
7. Chew like rat
8. Rekindle
9. Sidesteps
12. Imbiber
15. Transplanted (skin)
19. Carrion-eating animals
21. Entranceway chimes
22. Precious metal
23. Paved enclosure
24. International agreements

DOWN

1. Pulled sharply
2. Unmarried
3. Land units
4. Trader
5. Navigational warning light
6. Witty conversation
10. Sector
11. Way out
12. Unexploded shell
13. Very dark
14. Oven for pottery
15. Happily
16. Dreaded
17. Result
18. Stage whispers
19. Split in two
20. Number of spider's legs

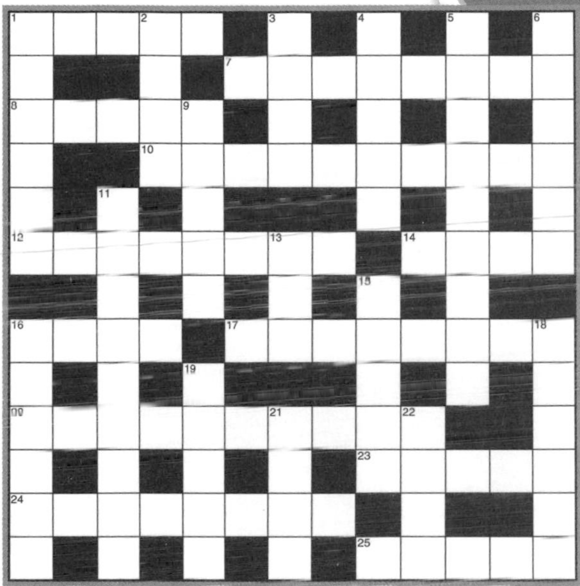

ACROSS

1. Inhale
7. Raised (design)
8. Around (that date)
10. Strengthening
12. Reflex movement
14. Low platform
16. Coral bank
17. Tactic
20. Assured
23. Intimidate
24. Immobility
25. Slides

DOWN

1. Portion of circle
2. Proven truth
3. Complacent
4. Roamed
5. Roughly calculated
6. Proverbs
9. Main artery
11. Video photographer
13. Elect
15. Walked in water
16. Win back
18. Teenage people
19. Floats on breeze
21. Utensil
22. Poorly-lit

CROSSWORD 106

ACROSS

1. Novelists
4. Sober
7. People from Calcutta
8. Move with effort
9. Parish ministers
12. Earphone units
15. Issued (from)
17. Astonished
18. Locates
21. Cellophane cover
22. Give birth (of dog)
23. Retaliated for

DOWN

1. Set in motion
2. Aircraft shed
3. Hit with hand
4. Waist ribbon
5. Embarrassed
6. Bird of peace
10. Gun blasts
11. Bamboo-eating mammal
13. Depressed
14. Great slaughter
16. Inn
18. Went by air
19. Exchange
20. Statistics

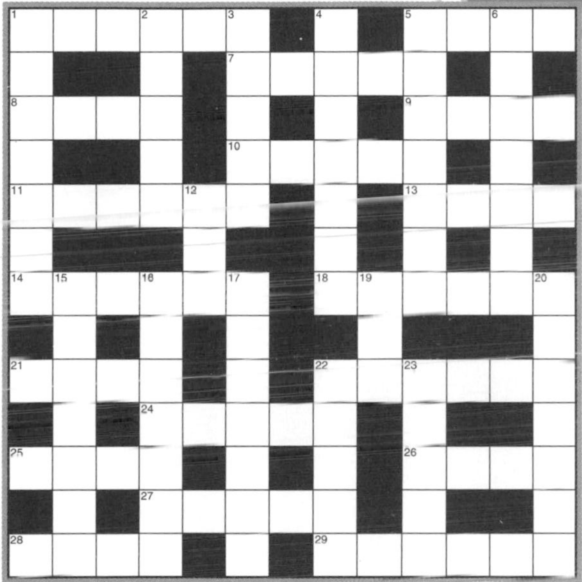

ACROSS

1. Mouth roof
5. Produces (egg)
7. Ocean mammal
8. Hoarse sound
9. Invalid
10. Bake in oven
11. Opponents
13. Part of eye
14. Sloops or ketches
18. Plan
21. Horse's gait
22. Gold lump
24. Send abroad in disgrace
25. Kitchen professional
26. Loose flesh
27. Not healthy
28. Iridescent gem
29. Fume

DOWN

1. Play the part of
2. First Greek letter
3. Washstand jugs
4. Made do
5. High-protein pulses
6. Shouting
12. Set fire to
15. Zeppelin
16. Detestable
17. Meet (requirements)
19. Australian bird
20. Significant
22. Ants' homes
23. Social blunder

ACROSS

1. Supplied funds for
5. Dam
7. Smear
8. Rissole
9. Acidity paper
12. Calling (of donkey)
15. Underground railway systems
19. Perspires
21. Intermittently
22. Speechless
23. Aromatic herb
24. Cannier

DOWN

1. Violin
2. Soundtrack CD
3. Arrives
4. Desk compartment
5. Unstable
6. Reigning
10. Burial chamber
11. Forearm bone
12. Commuter vehicle
13. Affirm
14. Novel thought
15. Rode on wave
16. Dire
17. Gives way
18. Map pressure line
19. Wilier
20. Bequeath

ACROSS

1. Skewered meat dish
7. Housing loan
8. Should, ... to
10. Purposely overhears
12. Dingier
14. Major Indonesian isle
16. Green gemstone
17. Piercing with spear
20. Full-length
23. Of sound
24. Quivers
25. Proposal

DOWN

1. Raps
2. Dull pain
3. Hand (out)
4. Breeding males
5. Wide (view)
6. Japanese hostess
9. Brindled cat
11. Wood smoothing sheet
13. Shady tree
15. Titled ladies
16. Lively
18. Food retailer
19. Beetle larvae
21. Antlered animal
22. Remove (hat)

CROSSWORD 110

ACROSS

1. Prolonged applause
4. Spongy growths
7. Bathroom fixture
8. Hidden supply
9. Unspoken
12. Be visible once more
15. Christmas season
17. Subtle shade of meaning
18. Shipment of goods
21. Senselessly
22. Waits, ... one's time
23. Please

DOWN

1. Tribute to deceased
2. Little crowns
3. Immature lice
4. Untruths
5. Contradicted
6. Linear unit
10. Exhaust
11. Loaded down
13. Herb
14. Given warning
16. Money case
18. Grooming tool
19. Painting medium
20. Vocalised

ACROSS

1. Rubs until sore
5. Public garden
7. Encrypts
8. Strong wind
9. Meditation routine
10. Hysteria
11. Meal course
13. Dagger handle
14. UFO, flying ...
18. Living in a group
21. While
22. Exchanged
24. Track down
25. Unit of weight
26. Take on (staff)
27. Aunt's husband
28. Night sky object
29. Eventuates

DOWN

1. Young swans
2. More at liberty
3. Range
4. Weirdness
5. Clairvoyant
6. Splendid clothes
12. Supplement, ... out
15. Religious non-believer
16. Map line
17. Return game
19. Belonging to us
20. Portable steps
22. Native American tent
23. Fire remains

CROSSWORD 112

ACROSS

1. Profession
5. Minuscule amount
7. Seep out
8. Tomb inscriptions
9. Gives speech
12. Teach
15. Wardrobe assistant
19. Extreme
21. Brought upon oneself
22. Starched neck frill
23. Solitary
24. Tennis court marking

DOWN

1. Haitian witchcraft
2. Turn aside
3. Articles
4. Pinned (down)
5. Sloping (typeface)
6. Guarantee
10. Pimples
11. Rams' mates
12. Tip of grain
13. Component
14. Car
15. Refusal
16. Military greeting
17. Wields
18. Repress
19. Unzipped
20. Ethical

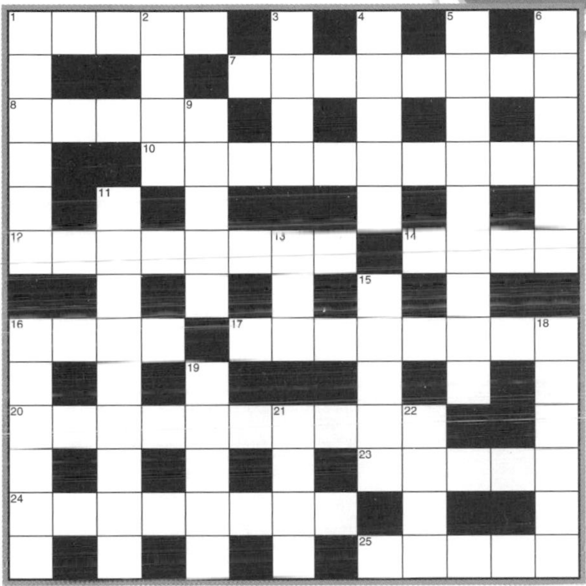

ACROSS

1. Higher (part)
7. Orators
8. Native animals
10. Stock market risk-taker
12. Impasse
14. Slay
16. Hatchets
17. Amorous
20. People in books
23. Pulls sharply
24. Made beloved
25. Glide on ice

DOWN

1. Open out
2. Immense time spans
3. Big-scale movie
4. Sends
5. Constrains
6. Celestial
9. Orchard fruit
11. Radio frequencies
13. Dove call
15. Small magical being
16. Arrow marksman
18. Pure
19. Plane detector
21. Foot digits
22. Subsided

CROSSWORD 114

ACROSS

1. Trivial objection
4. Dice shapes
7. Sediment
8. Rise to feet
9. Lives
12. Bee colonies
15. Technical drawings
17. Pass (of time)
18. Covered in foliage
21. Flew around (planet)
22. Flair
23. Shattered

DOWN

1. Shook with anticipation
2. Chest
3. Whirlpool
4. Billiard rods
5. Living plant collections, ... Gardens
6. Dashed
10. Actress, ... Jessica Parker
11. Wash soap from
13. Torn to strips
14. Card game
16. Ring-shaped rolls
18. Watch
19. Yellow part of egg
20. Curved-bill wading bird

ACROSS

1. Pakistan's ... Pass
5. Bird's bill
7. Senior
8. Fencing sword
9. Upper limbs
10. Long claw
11. Secretes
13. Be brave enough
14. Leafy side dishes
18. Comforting squeeze
21. Parsley or mint
22. Innate
24. Riled
25. Chesspiece
26. Wild pig
27. Surpass
28. Hawaiian garlands
29. Threw

DOWN

1. Zoo custodians
2. Mix
3. Hires out
4. Perfect
5. Marked (cattle)
6. Navy chief
12. Finish
15. Normal
16. Pure white animals
17. Eyeball hollows
19. Large vase
20. Survived
22. Simpleton
23. Infants

CROSSWORD 116

ACROSS

1. Keep apart
5. Rove
7. Sodium bicarbonate, baking ...
8. Scrambles up
9. Go beyond
12. Climbs
15. Bandits
19. Slumbering
21. Minor dispute
22. Clothed
23. Nominate
24. Colonists

DOWN

1. Female sibling
2. Die down
3. Curved over
4. Praises highly
5. Partial refund
6. Stoneworkers
10. Social group
11. Edgy, ill at ...
12. Horse-like animal
13. Cries like crow
14. Roman IX
15. Motive
16. Act properly
17. Jewish scholars
18. Digging tools
19. Delegate
20. Regional

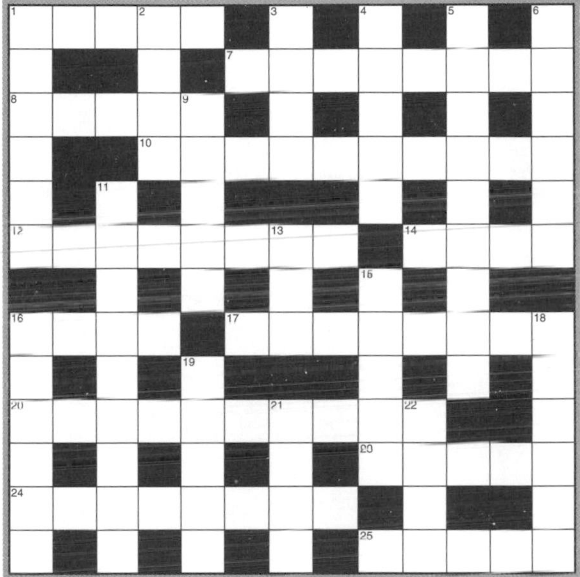

ACROSS

1. Bordered
7. Bird's width
8. Variety of animal
10. Moons
12. Lack of generosity
14. Bring bad luck to
16. Honey wine
17. Elongate
20. Long-standing customs
23. Baking agent
24. Rocky projections
25. Moving about

DOWN

1. Preserve (corpse)
2. Sight organs
3. Infuriate
4. Sprightly
5. Powerful beam
6. For men or women
9. Intimidate
11. Waterfalls
13. Feminine pronoun
15. Severe pain
16. Small celestial body
18. Flower syrup
19. Tempestuous
21. Little devils
22. Observes

CROSSWORD 118

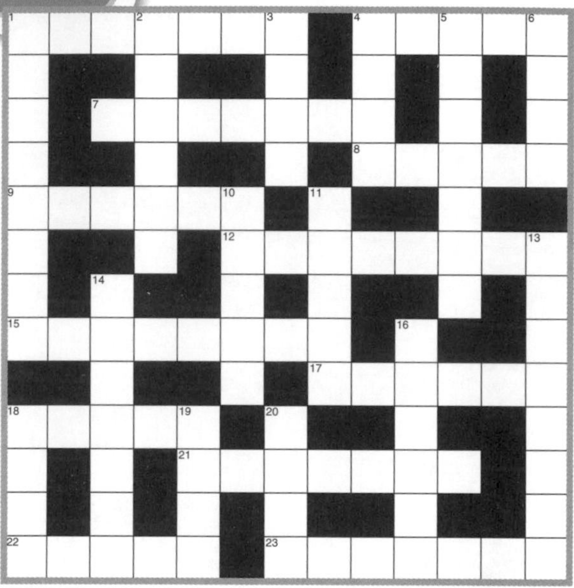

ACROSS

1. Female thespian
4. Blood-cleaning organ
7. Mopped
8. College tests
9. Alerted
12. Partaking of alcohol
15. Ice rivers
17. Terrified
18. Tycoon
21. Greed
22. Roman garments
23. Fidget, ... one's thumbs

DOWN

1. Letting
2. Using oars
3. Tearful gasps
4. Vein of ore
5. B6 or thiamine
6. Football arbiters
10. Leapt into water
11. Gulf
13. Instruction
14. Silencing
16. Putrid
18. Grain product
19. Trails (behind)
20. Viral skin growth

ACROSS

1. Covered-in canoes
5. Spiders' traps
7. Make on loom
8. Pip
9. Musical, My Fair ...
10. Hormone organ
11. Drives forward
13. Freezes, ... over
14. Vehicle depot
18. Absorb (food)
21. Tiny landmass
22. Spiritualist's meeting
24. Wooden post
25. Brave man
26. Bee nest
27. Small insect
28. Present
29. Spiral nails

DOWN

1. Touching with lips
2. Confuse
3. Takes large swallow
4. Pillaged
5. Fusing (metal)
6. Financial estimates
12. Ship's diary
15. Harsh
16. Phenomenal
17. Chores
19. Rage
20. Wavers (on edge)
22. Genders
23. Detest

CROSSWORD 120

ACROSS

1. Squid
5. Chinese boat
7. Wharf
8. Spectacles supplier
9. Corroded
12. Peppermint essence
15. Foamed
19. Stopped
21. Mobile homes
22. Window ledge
23. Grain storage facility
24. Steams in the sun

DOWN

1. Truncheon
2. Invited
3. Dodge
4. Chant
5. Short coat
6. Dog shelter
10. Atop
11. Every single
12. BSE, ... cow disease
13. Facial feature
14. Witches
15. Garden barriers
16. Red salad fruit
17. School compositions
18. Grown-ups
19. Hindu social position
20. Valuable possession

ACROSS

1. Lamp
7. Daily (occurrence)
8. Pasture
10. Economic slump
12. Action-packed
14. Manner of walking
16. Clap (of thunder)
17. Illuminated (arena)
20. Perceiving wrongly
23. Violent criminals
24. Clemency
25. Used axe

DOWN

1. Hoisted
2. Grasp
3. Across
4. Body-search
5. Prudent
6. Swan chick
9. Decompose
11. Annoying
13. Sick
15. Hip or knee
16. Face blemish
18. Taunted
19. Yields
21. Ethnic group
22. Clarified butter

CROSSWORD 122

ACROSS
1. Genetically altered
4. Rubbed lightly
7. Protest banner
8. Pass (legislation)
9. Heathens
12. Pants
15. Fishing vessels
17. Deeply desires
18. Ear test, ... examination
21. Citrus fruits
22. Strange
23. Enormous

DOWN
1. Squandered
2. Not sinking
3. Haul
4. Broad
5. Royal homes
6. Song for two
10. Hard iron alloy
11. Loud
13. Bright weather
14. Bearer (of disease)
16. Thin biscuits
18. Wheel shaft
19. Taste defeat
20. Coconut tree

ACROSS

1. Droning insect
5. Stitched
7. Type of orange
8. Otherwise, or ...
9. Inscribe
10. Tied (shoes)
11. Set fire to
13. Developed
14. Scoundrel
18. Cease
21. Small vipers
22. Defective
24. Desk
25. Opinion survey
26. Flower container
27. Trimmed
28. Poems
29. Noiseless

DOWN

1. Twist pioneer, Chubby ...
2. Revise
3. Leg/foot joint
4. Ejected from home
5. Toboggans
6. Cricket bowler's targets
12. Meadow
15. Escape
16. Fortresses
17. Lower back pain
19. Conger or moray
20. Neatest
22. Supplies food to
23. Metal-working block

CROSSWORD 124

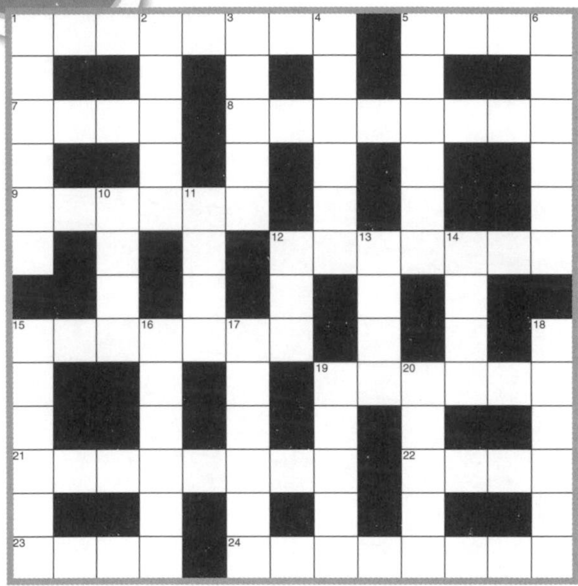

ACROSS

1. Contract killer
5. Cowl
7. Flamingo's hue
8. 12-month-old horse
9. Aircraft landing ground
12. Sentence structure
15. Oddly
19. More avid
21. Sprightliest
22. Soprano's solo
23. Wish
24. Anticipation

DOWN

1. Have ambitions
2. Lopsided
3. Coyly
4. In closer proximity to
5. Lighter-than-air gas
6. Short pointed knife
10. Wearing nothing
11. A distance
12. Anchoring rope
13. Helper
14. Most important
15. Slake (thirst)
16. Able to be eaten
17. Tiers
18. Invent
19. Flying toys
20. Fill with joy

ACROSS

1. Large jet plane
7. Fleece clippers
8. Twist (nose)
10. Hot season
12. Tactful person
14. Mutilate
16. Gave temporarily
17. Salvage
20. Uncultivated region
23. Mayhem
24. Land use entitlement
25. Devout

DOWN

1. Protruded
2. Foundation garments
3. Fake
4. Carnivals
5. Pledges
6. High regard
9. Personal glory
11. Lacking backbone
13. Gorilla or chimpanzee
15. Collision
16. Solicitor
18. Casts out
19. Fabric joins
21. No part
22. Indian dress

CROSSWORD 126

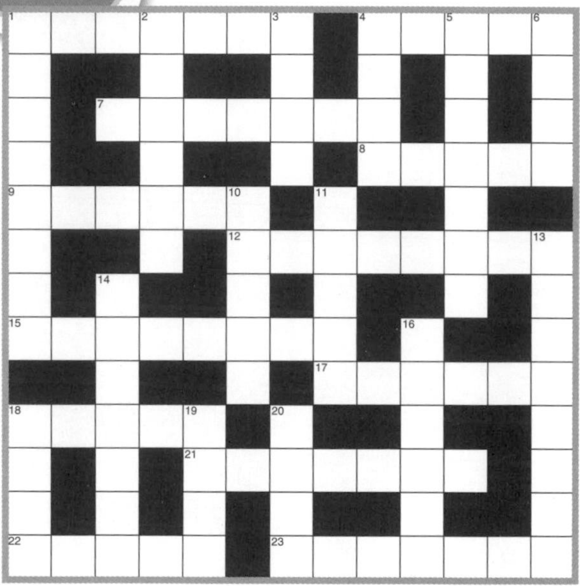

ACROSS

1. Absconded
4. 52-week intervals
7. Relapse in recovery
8. Diary record
9. Reimburse
12. Edge of highway
15. Port working vessels
17. Egg-yolk shade
18. Not sleeping
21. Took tiny bites from
22. Corroded
23. Drained contents of

DOWN

1. Person leaving native land
2. Boulevard
3. Small measure of spirits
4. Ox harness
5. Refrain (from)
6. Put to the sword
10. Fantasy
11. Viola flower
13. Wound together
14. Tropical lizards
16. Expressive
18. Slightly open
19. Resentful longing
20. Reed instrument

ACROSS

1. Has buoyancy
5. Cautious
7. Avoid (capture)
8. Tiny particle
9. Official stamp
10. Jumped up
11. Hostile crowds
13. Prepare for publication
14. Cleans by rubbing hard
18. Queuing, ... up
21. Hitch
22. Detour round
24. Freedom fighter
25. Bass brass instrument
26. Match before final
27. Await with horror
28. Forest plant
29. Enforces (payment)

DOWN

1. Camera lights
2. Intended
3. Trades for cash
4. Sun umbrella
5. US frontier movie
6. Straighten again
12. Outgoing flow, ... tide
15. Overcome
16. Improve in quality
17. Skin mite rash
19. Very cold
20. Talks idly
22. Knife's cutting edge
23. Italian food

CROSSWORD 128

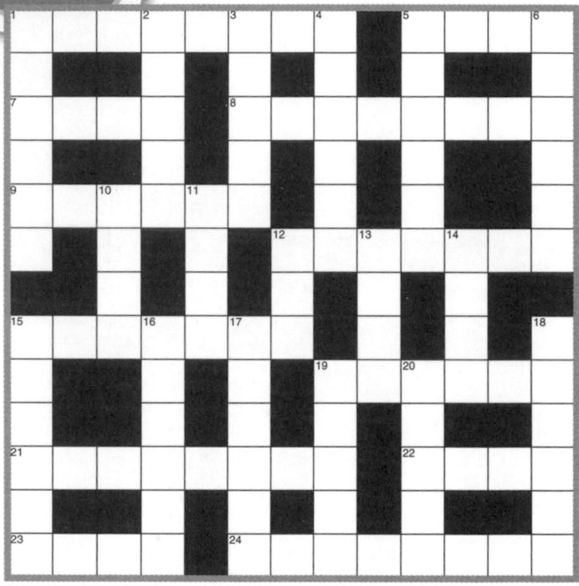

ACROSS

1. In these times
5. Inactive
7. Intellect
8. Inspired with reverence
9. Coral island lake
12. Unfastens
15. Spun
19. Paltry
21. Enumerated
22. False belief
23. Knocks sharply
24. Site

DOWN

1. Unfeelingly
2. Related to hearing
3. Oak nut
4. Dual-sound system
5. Reflections
6. Bestows
10. Essence of matter
11. Unseat
12. Youngster
13. On an occasion
14. Large deer
15. Marathon competitor
16. Courtroom excuses
17. Ensnare
18. Punctuation mark
19. Styles
20. Allow inside

ACROSS

1. Belt hole
7. Malarial insect
8. Appeal earnestly
10. Price negotiation
12. Making possible for
14. Slip sideways
16. Tasks
17. Not merited
20. Fashionable society people
23. Bird of prey
24. Passenger lift
25. Work (dough)

DOWN

1. Teat
2. Seaside crustacean
3. Dinner chime
4. Provide with gear
5. Aping
6. Wedged
9. Every 24 hours
11. Cooked outdoors
13. Convent dweller
15. Wage recipient
16. Medieval king's clown
18. Protect
19. Suez or Panama
21. Press (clothes)
22. Milled (timber)

CROSSWORD 130

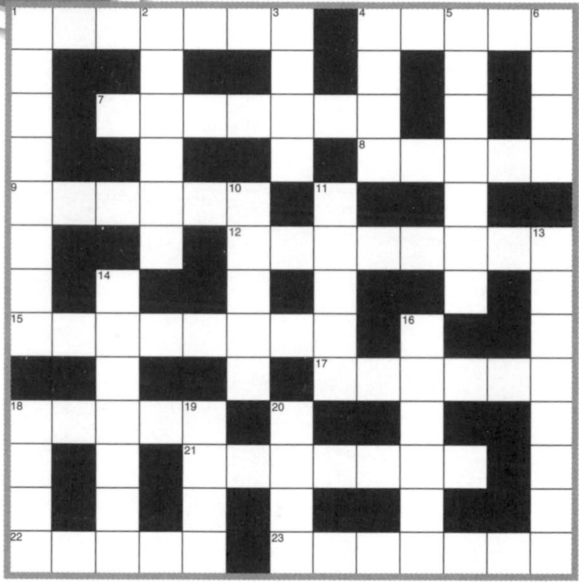

ACROSS

1. Of water
4. Wild
7. Stares angrily
8. Cardiac organ
9. Possessed jointly
12. Rate
15. Naval clergyman
17. Deep shock
18. Gallantly
21. Stretchy material
22. Hard to climb
23. Responded

DOWN

1. Non-amplified (guitar)
2. Attraction
3. Musical symbol
4. Marine creature
5. Absconder
6. Departed
10. Postpone
11. Contaminate
13. Pitched tents
14. Leaf vegetable
16. Harry Potter actor, ... Radcliffe
18. Bobs head
19. Dog's cry
20. Twosome

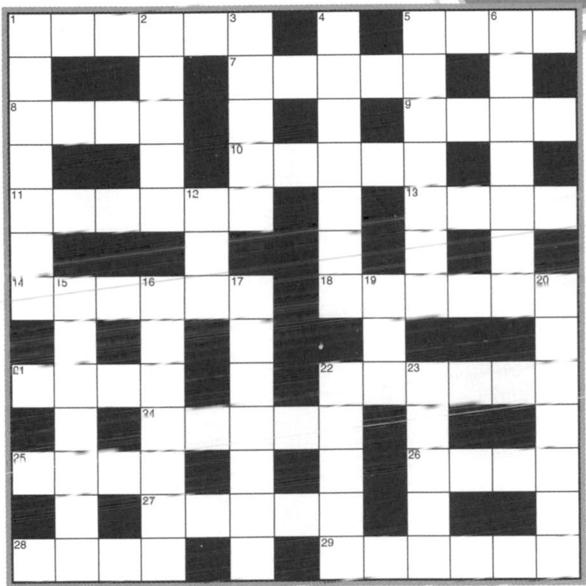

ACROSS

1. Sputter
5. Availed oneself of
7. More enjoyable
8. Ewe's offspring
9. Baby bears
10. Soil-enriching mixture
11. Notoriety
13. Object of worship
14. Huge star cluster
18. In conclusion
21. Aura
22. Breathe noisily
24. Hidden
25. Sinister sign
26. Became mature
27. Levels
28. Says further
29. Poured

DOWN

1. Toppling
2. African striped animal
3. Adversary
4. Surgeon's knife
5. Spiny creatures, sea ...
6. Involve (in dispute)
12. Blend
15. Frightened
16. Puts oil on
17. Not as old
19. Fire powder
20. Surrendered
22. Arm/hand joint
23. Eradicate

CROSSWORD 132

ACROSS

1. Menace
5. Single sound system
7. Mexican food shell
8. Saying yes
9. Commands
12. Team participants
15. Kept balls in air
19. Pearl source
21. Marooned
22. Small pool
23. A selection
24. Miscellaneous items

DOWN

1. Skin decoration
2. Run off to marry
3. Bangkok natives
4. Ordinary
5. Humbly
6. Kidneys, liver & lungs
10. Cow excrement
11. Genuine
12. Bean container
13. Crooked
14. North, south, ..., west
15. Floor beams
16. Rotate
17. Evades
18. Barters
19. Ancient
20. Wonderful

ACROSS

1. Sailing boat
7. Occasion
8. Light purple
10. Evil
12. Swamped by sound
14. Purges
16. Woe!
17. Soberly
20. Mariner's skill
23. Unite
24. Role models
25. Open tarts

DOWN

1. Screamed
2. Top of body
3. Class-conscious person
4. Accounts
5. Uses adjectives
6. House support poles
9. Commends (for bravery)
11. Twin-hulled vessel
13. Mother sheep
15. Adage
16. Plane corridors
18. Warbles alpine-style
19. Becomes distorted
21. Lose (fur)
22. Rind

CROSSWORD 134

ACROSS

1. Contaminate (environment)
4. Little crown
7. Investigated furtively
8. Jostle
9. Leg bone
12. Shepherd's canine
15. Task-completion date
17. Harvester
18. Garbage
21. Collected
22. Pushes (shirt in)
23. Lubricates

DOWN

1. Appeased
2. Form a queue (4,2)
3. Glimpse
4. Ocean's flow
5. Anyone
6. Afresh
10. In a state of activity
11. JM Barrie play, ... Pan
13. Connoisseurs of food
14. Over-zealous supporter
16. Photographer's tool
18. Stretched firm
19. Coverings for head
20. Vampire's tooth

ACROSS

1. Sharply serrated
5. Spaces (between)
7. Proverb
8. Back of neck
9. Article
10. Sports squads
11. Possessors
13. Restore to health
14. Liquid toppings
18. Made home in tree
21. Mast pole
22. Ethnic bias
24. Copy outline of
25. Festive occasion
26. Tired reflex
27. Creative thoughts
28. Prisoner's room
29. Praises

DOWN

1. Minors
2. Adult goslings
3. Moves suddenly
4. Model of virtue
5. Japanese hostesses
6. Prelude
12. Wild grass
15. Placate
16. Cut short
17. Wandered off course
19. Geological age
20. Forceful requests
22. Recycle
23. Church cellar

CROSSWORD 136

ACROSS

1. Make familiar
5. Wicked
7. Empty space
8. Clutching
9. Fairly modern
12. Attentively
15. Examine
19. Vitality
21. Improves
22. Bridal headwear
23. In no peril
24. Struggled against

DOWN

1. Verb modifier
2. Improper
3. Gold brick
4. Journey
5. Glowing coals
6. Heritage
10. Drinking vessels
11. Plant stem lump
12. Child's bed
13. Unfasten
14. Large jug
15. Deduces
16. Procession
17. Agree
18. Rode bicycle
19. Lessens
20. Imps

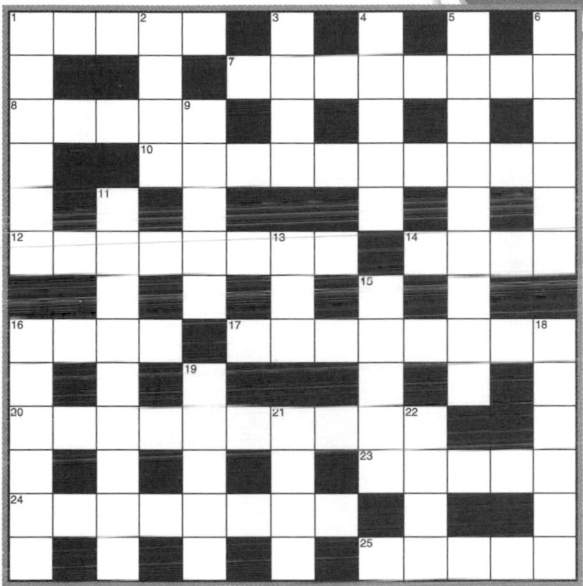

ACROSS

1. Cutting utensil
7. Most rigid
8. Postage sticker
10. Making longer
12. Furthest back
14. Tiny insects
16. Metric weight unit
17. Incapacitated
20. Unnecessarily
23. Adolescent
24. Prominence
25. Earlier

DOWN

1. Jewish food custom
2. Celebrity status
3. Stupefy
4. Edible innards
5. Boldly
6. Periods of growth
9. Stone fruits
11. Medical support worker
13. Slide on snow
15. Unhappily
16. Armed gangsters
18. Act indecisively
19. Narrow lane
21. Nauseous
22. Belonging to you

CROSSWORD 138

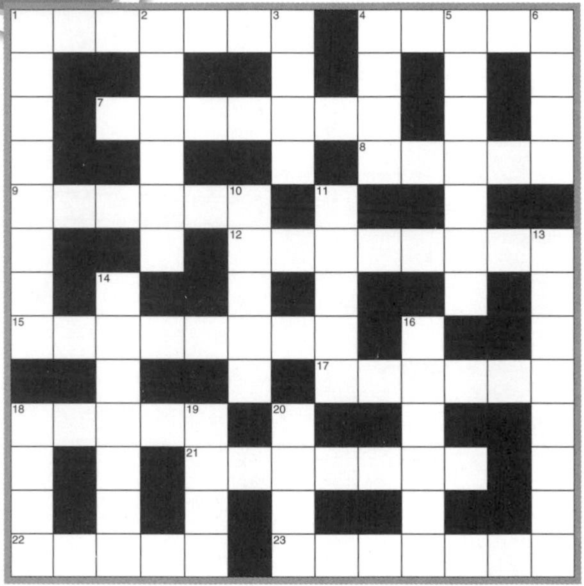

ACROSS

1. Cover up
4. Denim trousers
7. Miser
8. Endorses
9. Complete
12. Negative consequence
15. Units of sound
17. Non-transparent
18. Music style, rhythm and ...
21. Release from restraints
22. Grew dim
23. Scanning book

DOWN

1. Relinquished
2. Reviewer
3. Foliage part
4. Martial art
5. Chronicle
6. Depletes
10. Outside limits
11. Noosed rope
13. Resting on knees
14. Person charged with crime
16. Formed a crowd
18. Polish
19. Prosecuted
20. Go out of focus

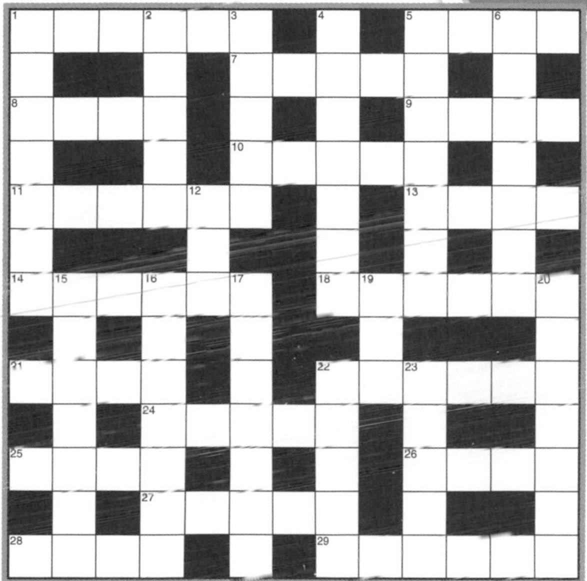

ACROSS

1. Feeling pain
5. Negative votes
7. Speak to crowd
8. Horseback sport
9. Subside
10. Preliminary copy
11. Runs after
13. Pork cut
14. African wildlife tour
18. Prescribed amount
21. Stepped (on)
22. Routines
24. Bring together
25. Group of three
26. Illuminating gas
27. Court attendant
28. Nocturnal birds
29. Veer sharply

DOWN

1. Features
2. Cultural symbols
3. Commodities
4. Parked undercover
5. Lies snugly
6. Tugging
12. Misjudge
15. Flight staff
16. Strenuous
17. Intuition
19. Eggs
20. Concentrated scent
22. Inheritors
23. Spree

CROSSWORD 140

ACROSS

1. Risked
5. Looked at
7. Roman garment
8. Adolescent
9. Lodges deeply
12. Requiring
15. Very old
19. Entertained
21. Crowded
22. Approach
23. Spun thread
24. Douse

DOWN

1. Loathing
2. Astound
3. Removes moisture from
4. Dent in cheek
5. Prolong
6. Tinting
10. Political power group
11. Love excessively, ... on
12. Negative adverb
13. Written test
14. Printing fluids
15. Lack of interest
16. Congenital
17. Horse calls
18. Stick (to)
19. Financial records check
20. Mouth sore

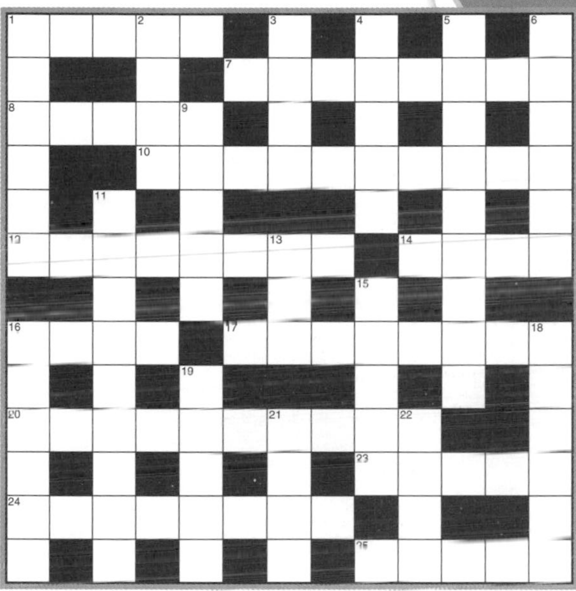

ACROSS

1. Fine display
7. Internally
8. As a result
10. German cabbage dish
12. Body preserver
14. Solid
16. Gated canal section
17. Overly precise
20. Field glasses
23. Gush
24. Offal
25. Sacred poem

DOWN

1. For some time
2. Curved lines
3. AM, ... meridiem
4. Songbirds
5. Perfectionists
6. Method
9. Too soon
11. Vulgar comment
13. December 31, New Year's ...
15. Scalp strands
16. Hit ball high
18. Tribal convention
19. Atlantic or Pacific
21. Recline lazily
22. Mineral springs

CROSSWORD 142

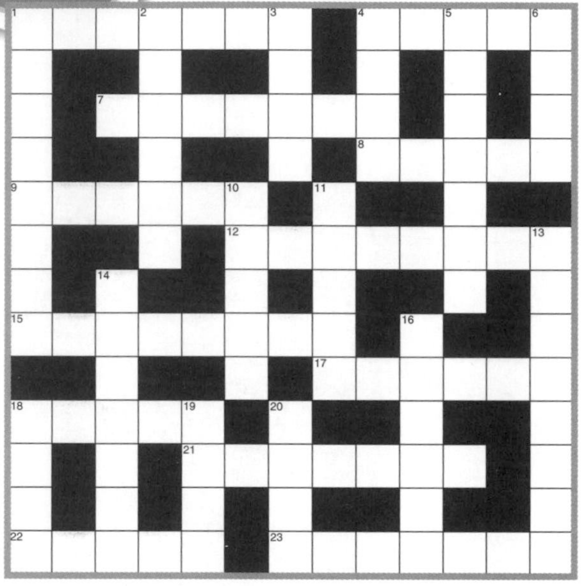

ACROSS

1. Foyers
4. Act of foolishness
7. Aircraft attendant
8. Mops (deck)
9. Tile-chip picture
12. Refugees
15. Stalkers
17. Degraded
18. Public square
21. Ringing (of bell)
22. Stage of development
23. Crossing (river)

DOWN

1. Connective tissue
2. Be disloyal to
3. Yacht pole
4. Short-lived trends
5. Situated
6. Tropical root vegetables
10. Surrendered
11. Light timber
13. Pacifying
14. Mosquito-borne fever
16. Showered
18. Inflate, ... up
19. Land measure
20. Petty quarrel

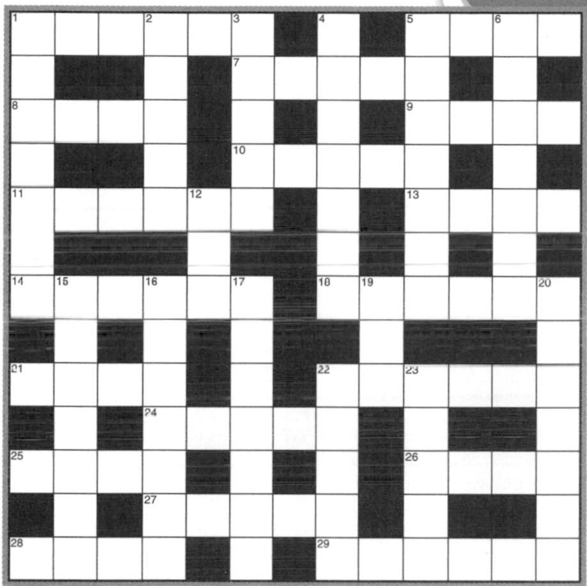

ACROSS

1. Village's population
5. Suitor
7. Thin candle
8. Musical pitch
9. Skin irritation
10. Curtain
11. Restive
13. Brave deed
14. More effortless
18. Be thrifty
21. Karate blow
22. Lessens
24. Circle (planet)
25. Load-bearing post
26. Become weary
27. Final figure
28. Rock band's sound boosters
29. Long-handled spoons

DOWN

1. Salad leaf vegetable
2. Rink
3. Learn for exam
4. Spreads out untidily
5. Shorter
6. Hail as
12. Witness (event)
15. Religious non-belief
16. Brings from overseas
17. Hare relatives
19. Male swan
20. Crayon drawings
22. Coral isle
23. Behaved

CROSSWORD 144

ACROSS

1. Tycoons
5. ... & papa
7. Girl's plaything
8. Fluid losses
9. Groaned
12. Funeral vehicles
15. Recently amended
19. Stinging insect
21. Ready to explode
22. Manufactured
23. Actor, ... Nolte
24. Re-evaluate

DOWN

1. Computer phone links
2. Synthetic fabric
3. Laid ceramic squares
4. Document fastener
5. More miserly
6. Valuable possessions
10. Corrosive substance
11. Let out (shriek)
12. Owned
13. Lowest female voice
14. Imminently
15. Irregular
16. Assail
17. Weirder
18. Says
19. 'Laughing' scavenger
20. Elevated walkways

CROSSWORD 145

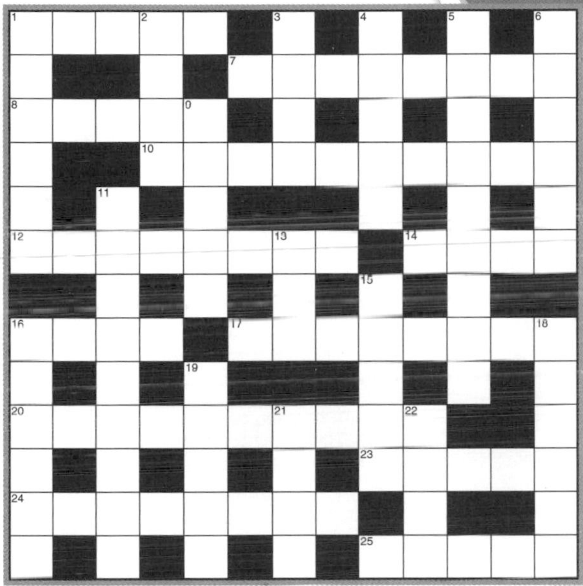

ACROSS

1. Take oath
7. Plane-jump sportsman
8. Phrase
10. Impartiality
12. Gaining knowledge
14. Recited
16. Niggles
17. Of metal
20. Countryside paintings
23. Foolishly idealistic
24. Puffed up
25. Genre

DOWN

1. Swirl
2. Unknown writer
3. Satirical sketch
4. Notions
5. Escapable
6. Tattered
9. Intends
11. Type of dive
13. Named before marriage
15. Shelter
16. Set in (design)
18. Cheddar or Edam
19. Hollywood award statuette
21. Gorillas or chimpanzees
22. Common seasoning

CROSSWORD 146

ACROSS

1. Sorcerers
4. Australian marsupial
7. Results
8. Steam burn
9. Remove from danger
12. Railway bridges
15. Pulled a face
17. Radio interference
18. Playing-card Jack
21. Embarrassed
22. Levels
23. Showed gratitude to

DOWN

1. Irrigating
2. Influence
3. Footwear item
4. Touch lips
5. Move forward
6. Between
10. Eject from home
11. Exalts
13. Dotted
14. Wondrous thing
16. Cave chamber
18. Flying toy
19. Wheat tips
20. Breathe rapidly

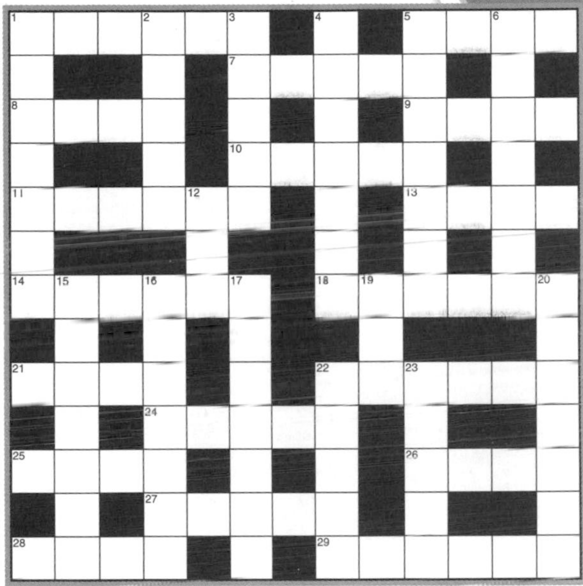

ACROSS

1. Iguana or monitor
5. Spheres
7. Ship's unloading site
8. Blocking vote
9. Heavy criticism
10. Gowns
11. Representing, on ... of
13. Snake-like fish
14. Chocolate choux pastry
18. Happened next
21. Door handle
22. Engraved with acid
24. Peru beast
25. Short skirt style
26. Impulse
27. Nook
28. Doe's mate
29. Discreetly

DOWN

1. Endearing
2. Smell
3. One of Snow White's friends
4. Rubbish
5. Counterbalances
6. Writing for visually impaired
12. Hawaiian garland
15. Comprise, ... of
16. Sauntering
17. Love affair
19. Almond or pecan
20. Feeble with age
22. Roof edges
23. Cake morsel

CROSSWORD 148

ACROSS

1. Announced
5. Bread unit
7. Narrated
8. Interfered
9. Person giving loan
12. Most frozen
15. Adolescence
19. Celebratory meals
21. Seized (aircraft)
22. Japanese wrestling style
23. Trick
24. Pirates' hoard

DOWN

1. Large inns
2. Helped
3. Discourage
4. Dotted game tile
5. Ogled, ... at
6. Move restlessly
10. Without sensation
11. On any occasion
12. Weep
13. Misplace
14. Hearing organs
15. Shoved
16. Enclose in box
17. Travel coupon
18. On dry land
19. Soft confection
20. Donkeys

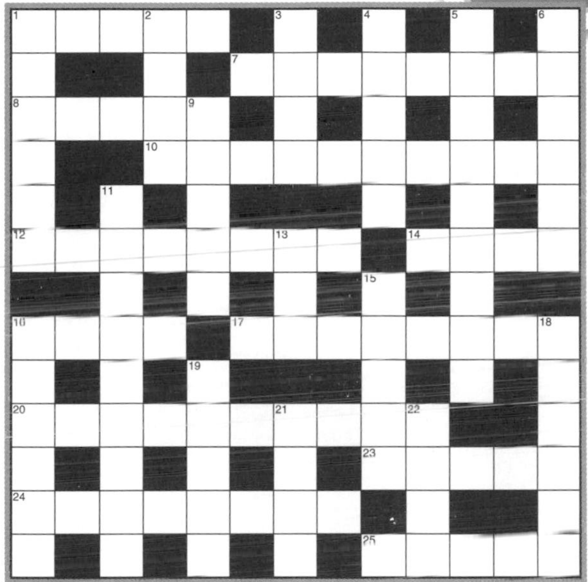

ACROSS

1. Adult girl
7. Restorer
8. Pasted
10. Man-made materials
12. Go underwater
14. Indication
16. Close
17. Ancient bead counters
20. Crockery
23. Enclosed areas
24. Octopus arm
25. Very pale

DOWN

1. Carts
2. Beers
3. Joke
4. Ring-shaped bun
5. Most intelligent
6. Cropped up
9. Dutch sea walls
11. Acquiring
13. Gossip
15. Frightening
16. State of undress
18. Add salt to
19. Four-door car
21. Join by fusion
22. Consumes

CROSSWORD 150

ACROSS

1. Made minor adjustments to
4. Sentry's spell of duty
7. Barber's clip
8. Cobra or boa
9. Patched
12. Confectionery covers
15. Crushed underfoot
17. Stuck down (envelope)
18. Recorded
21. Sloping typeface
22. Bravery decoration
23. Later

DOWN

1. Slimmest
2. Trophies
3. Pack of cards
4. Winery fermentation tanks
5. Regarded smugly
6. Medieval guitar
10. Resided
11. Attacks
13. Of poorer quality
14. Tasted
16. Waltzed
18. Those people
19. Clock face
20. Buggy

ACROSS

1. Oily
5. Catches (thief)
7. Exclusive group
8. Extinct bird
9. As well
10. Respond to stimulus
11. Detain during wartime
13. Terminates
14. Ransack
18. Picasso or da Vinci
21. Neglect
22. Frail
24. Outdo
25. Expensive
26. Doorpost
27. Fencing swords
28. Pedigree farm
29. Reaping tool

DOWN

1. Dizzier
2. Greatly love
3. Long (for)
4. Amazon river fish
5. Most orderly
6. In any case
12. Small blanket
15. Seat divider
16. Modified
17. Opted
19. Crustacean's eggs
20. Quiver
22. Dental thread
23. Take pleasure in

CROSSWORD 152

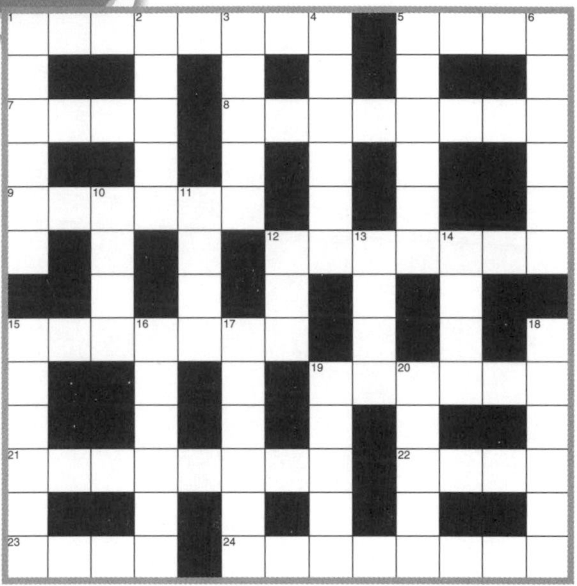

ACROSS

1. Address angrily
5. Travel permit
7. Sunrise
8. Inclinations
9. Expels from homeland
12. Sparked
15. Pamphlet
19. Stocking band
21. Six-sided figures
22. Calf meat
23. Rational
24. Expands

DOWN

1. Tree fences
2. Cancel
3. Strong winds
4. High-gloss paint
5. Expresses (opinion)
6. Ridiculous
10. Towards interior of
11. Noble rank
12. Overweight
13. Swedish pop group
14. Suggestion
15. Shrubs
16. Japanese martial art
17. Inter
18. Dental tools
19. Enthusiasm
20. Shouted, ranted & ...

ACROSS

1. Person, ... being
7. Plugs
8. Practice rifle cartridge
10. Jingling instrument
12. Originates (from)
14. Planted (of seeds)
16. Converse
17. Nuclear generators
20. Prescription dispensaries
23. Hurried
24. Intimidates
25. Falsified

DOWN

1. Famous space telescope
2. Parent's sister
3. Bang (toe)
4. Spurt
5. Punctuation mark
6. At rear of vessel
9. Inuit boat
11. Room décor material
13. Poet's word for before
15. Chillier
16. Walk quietly
18. Squalid
19. Smudge
21. Gnaw
22. Long narrative

CROSSWORD 154

ACROSS

1. Overdue
4. Fermented apple juice
7. Wet slightly
8. Expo, ... fair
9. Twelve-monthly
12. Taking (revenge)
15. Grains
17. Wiped out
18. Swallow fluid
21. Avoidance
22. Shelled gastropod
23. Red pepper spice

DOWN

1. Intimidating
2. On the plane
3. Obligation
4. 100th of dollar
5. Forceful
6. Part played
10. Screams
11. Minor transgression
13. Obtain degree
14. SW African republic
16. Coax
18. Adds soundtrack to
19. Ship's spine
20. Body powder

ACROSS

1. Threat
5. Twofold
7. Jewish pastor
8. Tulip or daffodil
9. Seethe
10. Verification
11. Small tower
13. Grecian vases
14. Haphazard
18. Teeter
21. Hawaiian dance
22. Glided on ice
24. Extend arm
25. Vehicle for hire
26. Toppled
27. Rectify (text)
28. Fewer
29. Barked in pain

DOWN

1. Gangster
2. Fossil resin
3. Explode (of volcano)
4. Rectangles
5. Disperse
6. Pungent gas
12. Sense of self
15. Worship
16. Daily record books
17. Administrator
19. Large deer
20. Walked like duck
22. Sheltered from sun
23. Abysmal

CROSSWORD 156

ACROSS

1. Massaging
5. Multiple-birth child
7. Canned fish
8. Nonprofessionals
9. Detest
12. Tribal leader
15. Pastures
19. Tendons
21. More humane
22. Courageous
23. Small, soft feathers
24. Admires

DOWN

1. Water boiler
2. Modify
3. Angry
4. Brief look
5. Waited in line
6. Refuse to acknowledge
10. Charismatic air
11. Brave man
12. Belonging to him
13. Opposed to
14. Fashion
15. Disguised
16. Benumb
17. More cautious
18. Incidental comments
19. Varieties
20. Aristocratic

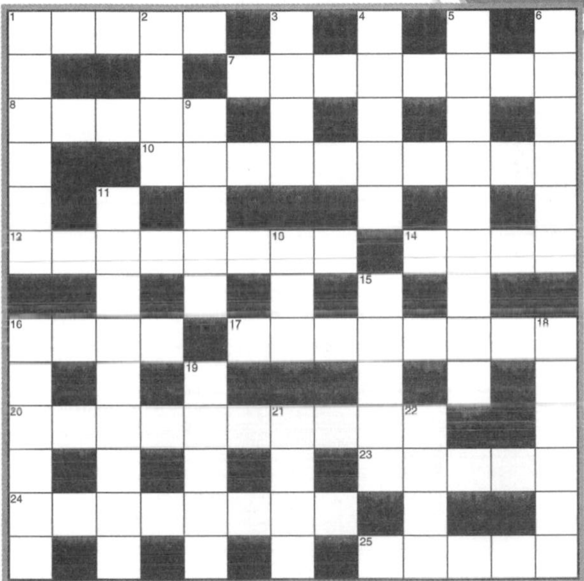

ACROSS

1. Blossom part
7. Illicit
8. Sixteenth of pound
10. Fast food snacks
12. Slimness
14. Tie with rope
16. Annoys constantly
17. Without deviation
20. Bring into accord
23. Frosting
24. Quick drawings
25. Noxious

DOWN

1. Launch forward
2. Curved span
3. Rebuff
4. Egypt's capital
5. Religious gifts
6. Shut
9. Receives as salary
11. Tidal zone trees
13. Movie filming area
15. Prickly desert plants
16. Kindest
18. Disastrous
19. Official decree
21. Necessity
22. Reflected sound

CROSSWORD 158

ACROSS

1. Antagonistic
4. Domain
7. Ancient
8. Laud
9. Spider's network
12. Handbills
15. Aromatic
17. Sailing boats
18. Stands on hind legs
21. Taller & thinner
22. Sum up
23. Floral memorial rings

DOWN

1. Shackle
2. Tossed
3. Ages
4. Paddy crop
5. Scrapes
6. Dissolve
10. Distend
11. Delicious
13. Pleasing to the senses
14. Overzealous supporter
16. Form of dermatitis
18. Lion's call
19. Hit with hand
20. Be familiar with

ACROSS

1. Royal home
5. Concert tour bookings
7. Huge sea mammal
8. Word indicating action
9. Lascivious
10. Refashioned
11. Hand digits
13. Fleur-de-lis plant
14. Impair
18. Occupy
21. Fifty per cent
22. Woodwind instruments
24. Cherub
25. Incendiary device
26. US wild cat
27. Thrust forward
28. Overblown publicity
29. Jockey's seat

DOWN

1. Hinged
2. Soundtrack CD
3. Large pitchers
4. Wound dressing
5. Castrated horse
6. Staring awkwardly
12. Quagmire
15. Physical structure science
16. Friendly
17. Graceful
19. Nothing
20. Put into bondage
22. Vents
23. Increased

CROSSWORD 160

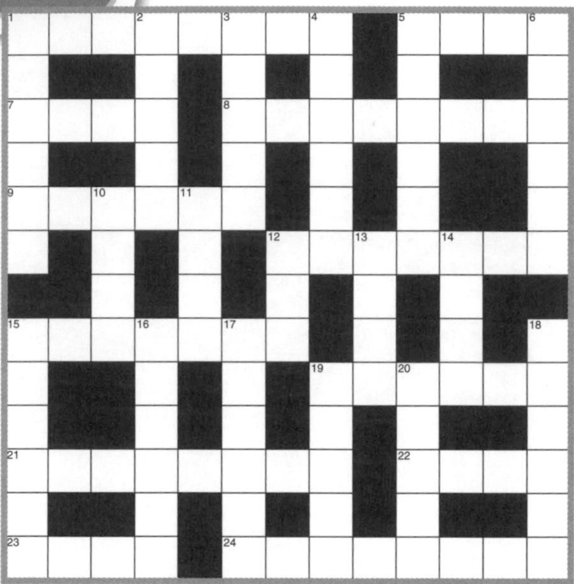

ACROSS

1. Witty reply
5. Imperial length unit
7. Charged particles
8. Abstained (from)
9. Lazy people
12. Shake
15. Cut into four
19. Straighten
21. Intestinal cleanser
22. Quick letter
23. Wearing shoes
24. House occupant

DOWN

1. Dried grape
2. Supermarket lane
3. Sea rhythms
4. Relieving
5. Demand
6. Crowd together
10. Tibetan priest
11. Pause
12. What we breathe
13. Symbolic picture
14. Suffer pain
15. Suppresses (fears)
16. Refunded
17. More nervous
18. Strangest
19. Consumers
20. Filleted

ACROSS

1. Morbid spectator
7. Underground room
8. Intellects
10. Infrequent
12. Children's vaulting game
14. After that
16. Multitudes
17. Bowling pins
20. Unvarying
23. Levied
24. Unnecessary
25. Frequently

DOWN

1. Cavort
2. Release (buttons)
3. Molten rock
4. Refurbish
5. At the same time
6. Pilfered
9. Scrape (shoes)
11. Outdoor grills
13. Acorn tree
15. Retard (growth)
16. Laments
18. Unexpected
19. Howls
21. Wind surge
22. Fish-landing pole

CROSSWORD 162

ACROSS

1. Unbridled
4. Humped animal
7. Assign
8. Glowing coal fragment
9. Rock levels
12. Not guilty
15. Cattle charge
17. Horse barn
18. Musical pace
21. Jumbled-word puzzle
22. Thaws
23. Applied therapy to

DOWN

1. Tools
2. Entreaty
3. Water bead
4. Mention as example
5. Speaks indistinctly
6. Suggestive look
10. Became ill
11. Largest body joints
13. Strung
14. Timber-cutting factory
16. Yellow fruit
18. Fixed period of time
19. Porridge cereal
20. Stop

ACROSS

1. Soak up
5. Not at home
7. Implant
8. Stare fixedly
9. Actor, ... Nicholson
10. Stringed instrument
11. Tangle up
13. Module
14. Vicious
18. Sharpening
21. Fruit peel
22. Leisurely walk
24. Musical drama
25. Soapy bubbles
26. Short office note
27. Summon up
28. Religious choral work
29. Waist bands

DOWN

1. Fishermen
2. Overweight
3. Backless seat
4. Eliminate
5. Take recess (of court)
6. Sale by bids
12. Slump
15. Divorce payment
16. Stomach
17. Wrap
19. Tennis umpire's call
20. Liquid measures
22. Bank vaults
23. Frolics

CROSSWORD 164

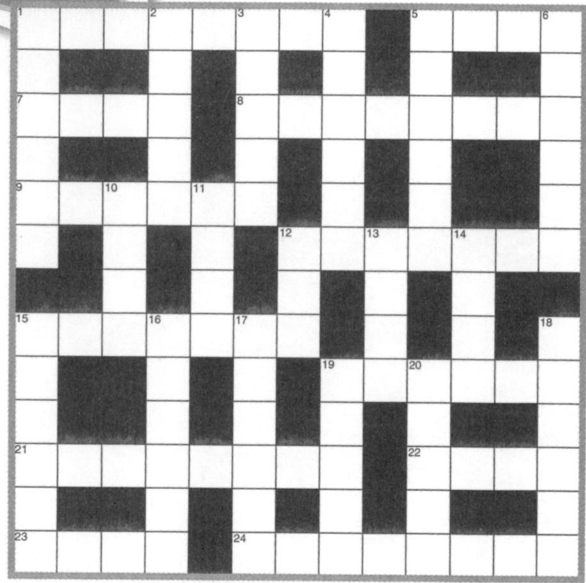

ACROSS

1. Disclosed
5. Male monarch
7. Hotels
8. Practical people
9. Roofing grass
12. Complain
15. Snuggled
19. Stoat-like animal
21. Losing blood
22. Dog's cry
23. Ready to harvest
24. Religious dissenters

DOWN

1. Floats on current
2. Disturb
3. Circumference
4. Trader
5. Chess horse
6. Engine seal
10. Classics studies
11. Loop
12. Helicopter landing area
13. Gape at
14. Slips up
15. Quantity
16. Steal
17. Improve the quality of
18. Snow crystals
19. Bet
20. Monastery superior

ACROSS

1. Tin or iron
7. Followed secretly
8. Imitate
10. Resolution of contract
12. Revive (interest)
14. Feat
16. Wedding promises
17. Unsightliness
20. Unlawful act
23. Detested
24. Cosmetic pencil
25. Glided on snow

DOWN

1. Club participant
2. Line of rotation
3. Voucher
4. Counted up
5. Sugared
6. Prepared for publication
9. Lebanese tree
11. Careless pedestrian
13. Poultry product
15. Breadth
16. Shrouded
18. Screened from sun
19. A second time
21. Untruths
22. Tug sharply

CROSSWORD 166

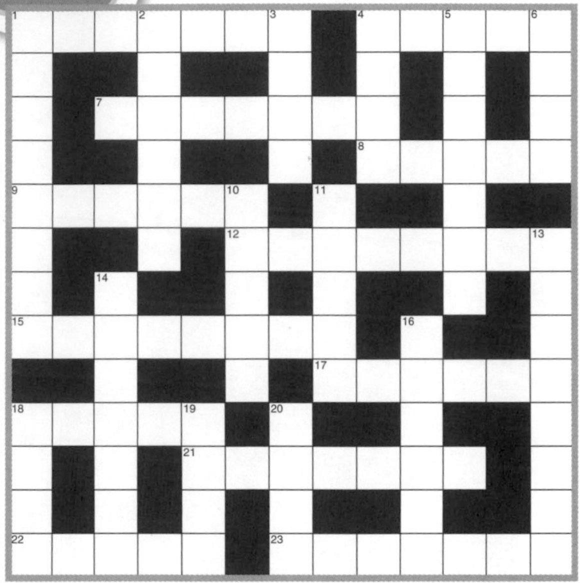

ACROSS

1. Gracefully stylish
4. Fundamental
7. Diabetic's preparation
8. Male duck
9. Return to custody
12. Resurface
15. Trainees
17. Allow
18. Tropical fruit
21. Envisage
22. Fights with fists
23. Obvious

DOWN

1. Outward
2. Amiable
3. Floor slate
4. 007 agent, James ...
5. Geometric shapes
6. Manage
10. Less wet
11. Make happen
13. Applicable
14. Self-contradictory statement
16. Sun-browned
18. Insincere (of speech)
19. Plans
20. Baked treat

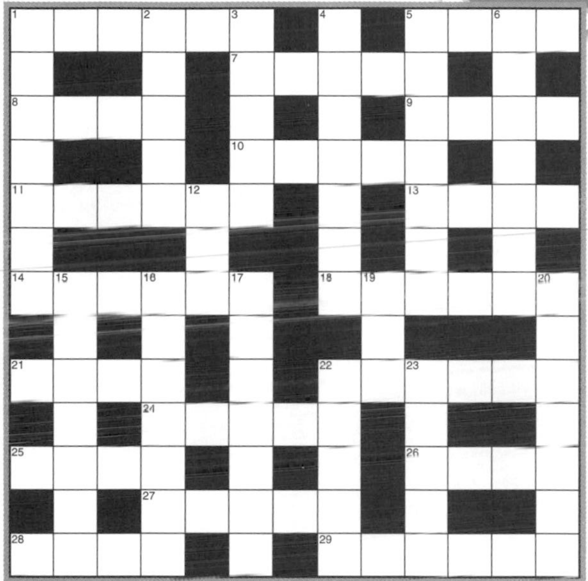

ACROSS

1. Posted
5. Enquires
7. Leavening agent
8. Average
9. Diplomacy
10. Light push
11. Crowd
13. Spike
14. Lettuce dishes
18. Couturier's drawing
21. Polluted air
22. Actor, ... Depardieu
24. Ruined Inca city, ... Picchu
25. Loyal
26. Slay
27. Requirements
28. Calm (sea)
29. Lobs

DOWN

1. 60-second periods
2. State of suspension
3. Becoming extinct, ... out
4. Loitered
5. Is present at
6. Striking with foot
12. Assent with head
15. Fleet's senior rank
16. Supplement
17. Aghast
19. Use frugally, ... out
20. Small lumps
22. Hotel patron
23. Lawn tools

CROSSWORD 168

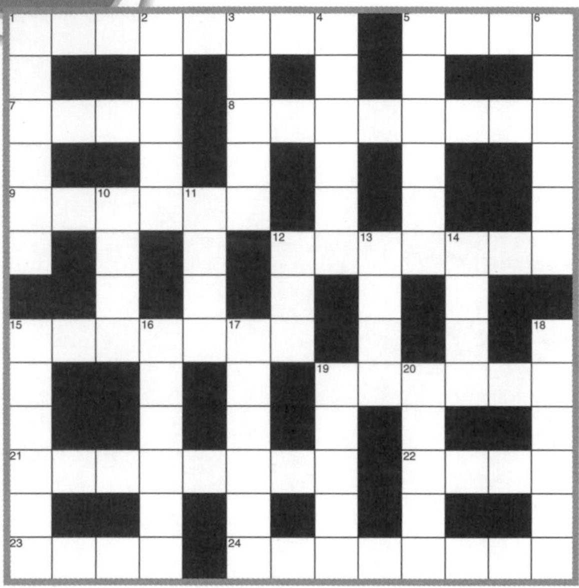

ACROSS

1. Increase in intensity
5. Timber
7. Loose hood
8. Rissole
9. Sitting down
12. Regards highly
15. Similar-meaning word
19. Tangled
21. Storyteller
22. Peruse quickly
23. Gyrate
24. Bath bubbles

DOWN

1. Absolve
2. Apportion
3. Carrying a gun
4. Greatly pleases
5. Teeter
6. Lags
10. Alike
11. Smooth
12. Spreading tree
13. Identical sibling
14. Way out
15. Steam-rooms
16. Sprint faster than
17. Adolescents
18. African scavengers
19. Fate
20. Desert water hole

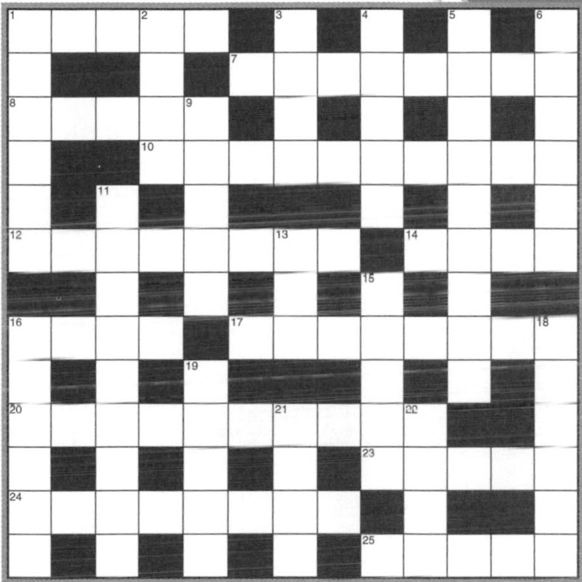

ACROSS

1. Kathmandu is there
7. Do trial run for
8. Not given food
10. Woven artworks
12. Collecting
14. Went quickly
16. Copied
17. Successes
20. Embroidery
23. Dirty-looking
24. In friendly way
25. Unadventurous

DOWN

1. Biliousness
2. Help (criminal)
3. In this place
4. Jokes
5. Rainwater runoff channel
6. Let for rent
9. Common flower
11. Dauntless stunt performer
13. And not
15. Sentry duty
16. Yearly
18. Moved from side to side
19. Sanitary
21. Healthy
22. Scottish skirt

CROSSWORD 170

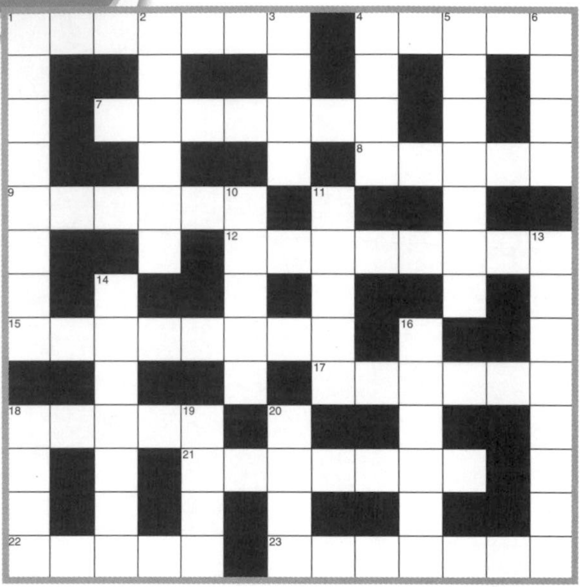

ACROSS
1. Card game
4. Relating to speech
7. Behave as glutton
8. Knowledge tests
9. Scowled
12. Granting
15. Most immature
17. Frightened
18. Supply sparingly
21. Hug
22. Female title
23. Herring relative

DOWN
1. Class
2. Verb modifier
3. Discontinued (project)
4. Cast ballot
5. Made of clay
6. Bottle tops
10. Calendar entries
11. Adds seasoning to
13. Leadership
14. Certified (accounts)
16. Bad (of butter)
18. Appear
19. Hair-wave treatment
20. Wading bird

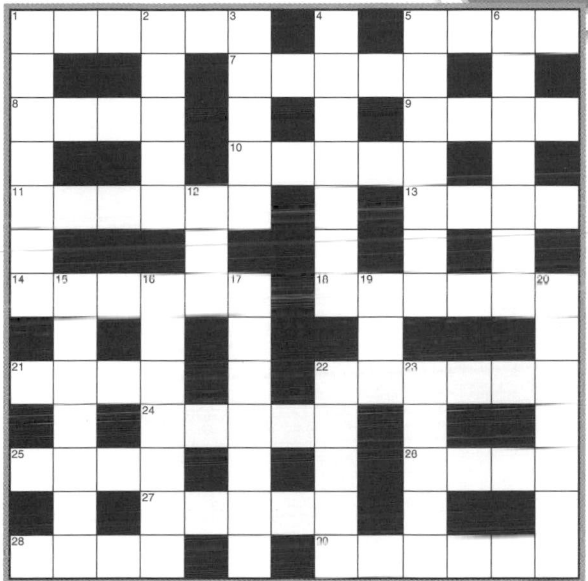

ACROSS

1. Find
5. Bat's flight limb
7. Member of jury
8. Meditation art
9. Iridescent gem
10. Metal links
11. Most recent
13. Merriment
14. Gaped
18. Army students
21. Write by machine
22. Frozen drip
24. Cut into cubes
25. Small mountain
26. Smug moralist
27. Painter's tripod
28. Lock openers
29. Completes (crossword)

DOWN

1. Allegiance
2. Degrade
3. Remove (DVD) from player
4. Naturally grown
5. Treated unfairly
6. Closest
12. Seek damages from
15. Whenever
16. Pine tree leaves
17. Debate
19. Circle portion
20. Snow vehicles
22. Cult heroes
23. Drive forward

CROSSWORD 172

ACROSS

1. Strategists
5. Fiji's capital
7. Rescue
8. Public addresses
9. Flow back
12. Book users
15. Most enthusiastic
19. Lewd man
21. Stepping (on)
22. Boulder
23. Eight, ..., ten
24. Nauseated

DOWN

1. Pie crust
2. Nephew's sister
3. Wear down
4. Deprive of food
5. Grinned
6. Evaluate
10. Arrived
11. Eat
12. Large rodent
13. Skilled
14. Every single
15. Young cat
16. Cancel out
17. Sequence
18. Slowed down (of vehicle)
19. Rationale
20. Sculpt (marble)

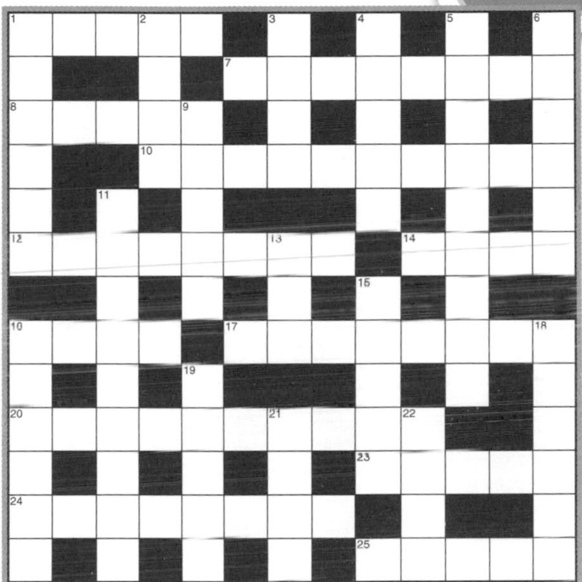

ACROSS

1. Passport endorsements
7. Comfortable seat
8. Gluttony
10. Most mischievous
12. Revolted
14. Filled with wonder
16. Extinct bird
17. Using DC power
20. Invalid's transport
23. Ballet
24. Switch
25. Salesman's pitch

DOWN

1. Less precise
2. Yemen port
3. Pull heavily
4. Severe (illness)
5. Documentation
6. Shredded
9. Dawdle
11. Subservience
13. Conger fish
15. Pungent
16. Arrived (of day)
18. Food grain
19. Entreaties
21. Pigs
22. Sloped walkway

CROSSWORD 174

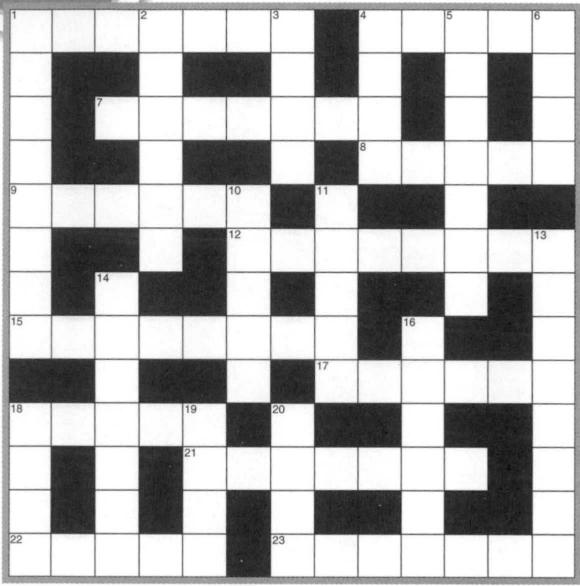

ACROSS
1. Crime against country
4. Instruct
7. Absolved
8. Declare
9. Nauseated
12. Lying ahead of
15. Arctic suicidal rodents
17. Escaped
18. Tested
21. Diary records
22. Plush toy, ... bear
23. Clothed in

DOWN
1. Placid
2. Lacking ethics
3. Tidy
4. Foot digits
5. Stomach-settling powder
6. In this place
10. Threads
11. Stop briefly
13. Resenting
14. Refereed
16. Profession
18. Canvas shelter
19. Openly resist
20. Store (cargo)

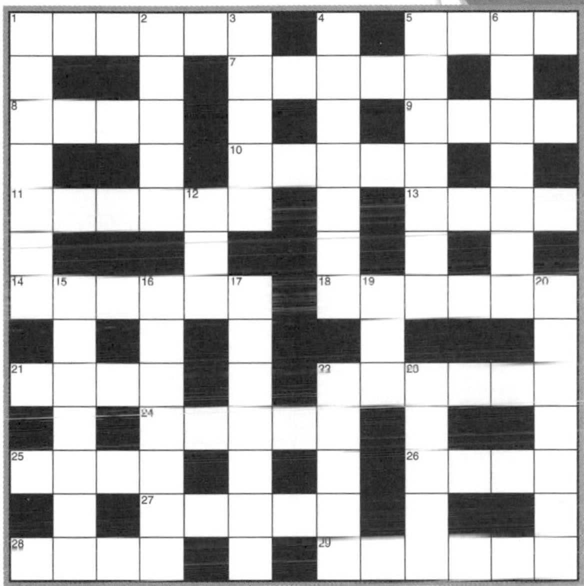

ACROSS

1. Banishes from school
5. Spoken
7. Requiring aid
8. Sear
9. Ballet, ... Lake
10. Skin transplant
11. Places in crypt
13. Small whirlpool
14. Vehicle depot
18. Feel aggrieved by
21. Wound encrustation
22. Underground stems
24. Senseless (comment)
25. Kiln
26. Tiny island
27. Happen
28. Egyptian cobras
29. Edges (towards)

DOWN

1. Inscribing
2. Ghostly
3. Hidden obstacles
4. US politician
5. Pearl-bearers
6. Discard
12. Oil-drilling platform
15. Recessed areas
16. Pure white animals
17. Enrich
19. Australian bird
20. Fringed cords
22. Eye droplets
23. Window shade

CROSSWORD 176

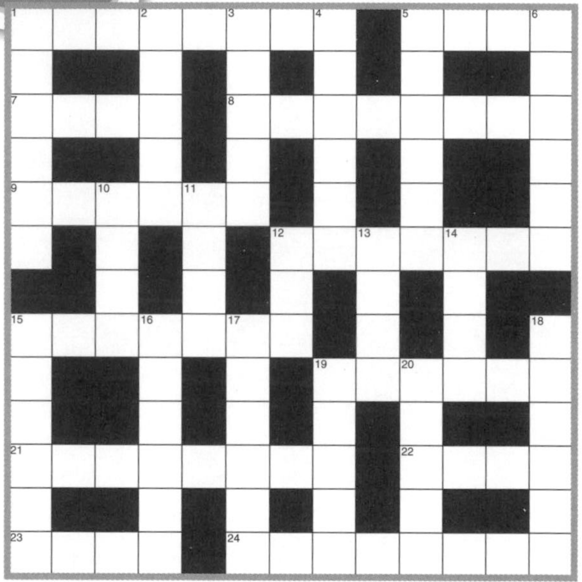

ACROSS

1. Bumping roughly
5. Paved enclosure
7. Oxen harness
8. Sailor
9. Outcome
12. Movie classifiers
15. Followed behind
19. Mouth sores
21. Most impetuous
22. Baby whale
23. Hindquarters
24. Of bone system

DOWN

1. Rapturous
2. Incisors or molars
3. Inserted piece
4. Quick look
5. Desires greatly
6. Forcible restraint
10. Cleaning agent, caustic ...
11. Elliptic
12. Atlantic fish
13. Invalid
14. Storybook monster
15. Attach with rope
16. Arch of foot
17. Goes in
18. Handy
19. Unhitch
20. Recurrent period

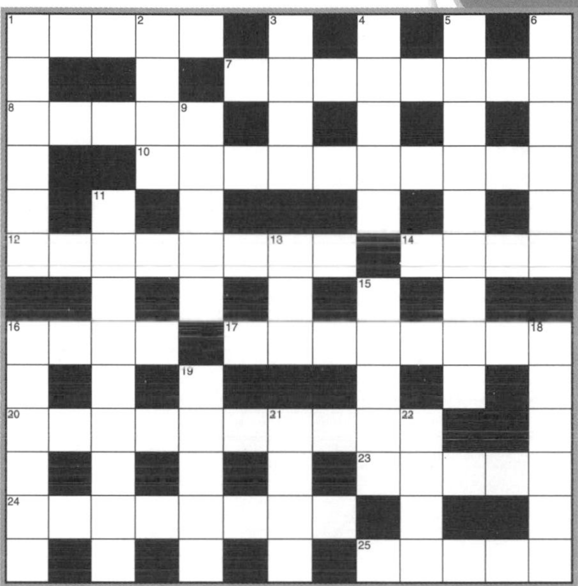

ACROSS

1. Fruit extract
7. Army rank
8. Small ships
10. Renowned performers
12. Exciting
14. Brass instrument
16. Travel by sea
17. Retrieves
20. People in book
23. Annual periods
24. Editing (text)
25. Lodge firmly

DOWN

1. Prodded
2. Infants' beds
3. Stirred from sleep
4. Muscle cramp
5. Prized
6. Blood component
9. Sweetener
11. Steered (course)
13. Wrath
15. Feel anxious
16. Used drinking straw
18. Pickled
19. Printed greetings
21. Heavy weights
22. Fabric join

CROSSWORD 178

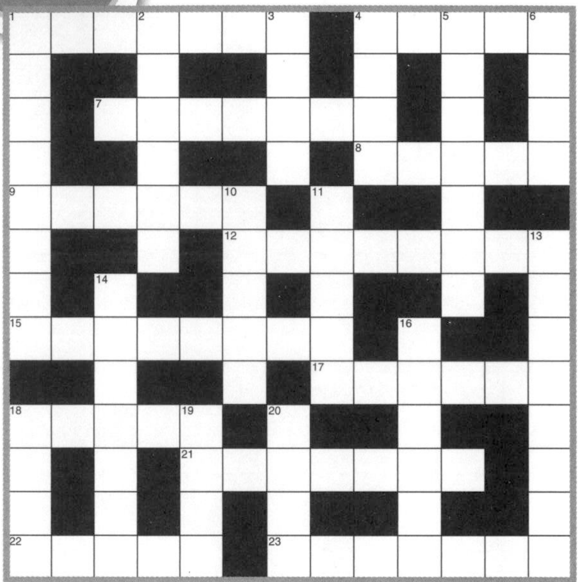

ACROSS

1. Clear (pipes)
4. Ill-suited
7. Well-known
8. Lessen
9. Thin covering
12. Opened (champagne)
15. Water-landing aircraft
17. Posture
18. Assistants
21. Subtleties of meaning
22. Roll (dice)
23. Of earthquakes

DOWN

1. Unearths
2. Lithe
3. Was familiar with
4. Minuscule amount
5. Assaults
6. Story
10. Pastoral
11. Land measures
13. Of the home
14. Dog trainer
16. Aspects
18. Border upon
19. Ice crystals
20. Goods trucks

ACROSS

1. Fiction books
5. Dry with cloth
7. Father's brother
8. Part of arrow
9. Sport squad
10. Instruct
11. Large migration
13. Make (profit)
14. Skill
18. Sprinted
21. Rein in
22. Principles
24. Proposition
25. Observe
26. Region
27. Banishment
28. Fix
29. Speckled

DOWN

1. Finest
2. Receded
3. Tailored ensembles
4. Grated
5. Moisture
6. Rolling grassland
12. Grecian pot
15. Rude
16. Jostled
17. Vehicular flow
19. As well as
20. Throw out
22. Peeved
23. Precise

CROSSWORD 180

ACROSS

1. Leaving empty
5. Cut with teeth
7. Forearm bone
8. Restraining (dog)
9. Tried
12. Selling
15. Heating bar
19. Pitch tent
21. Young plant
22. Necklace ball
23. Dimensions
24. Furthest limits

DOWN

1. Family tombs
2. Separate
3. Ran in neutral
4. Type of beard
5. Looked upon
6. Fringing
10. Wise person
11. Different
12. Animal physician
13. Part of speech
14. Suggestion
15. Obliterates
16. Halfway
17. Local inhabitant
18. Card suit
19. Octagon number
20. Steel rope

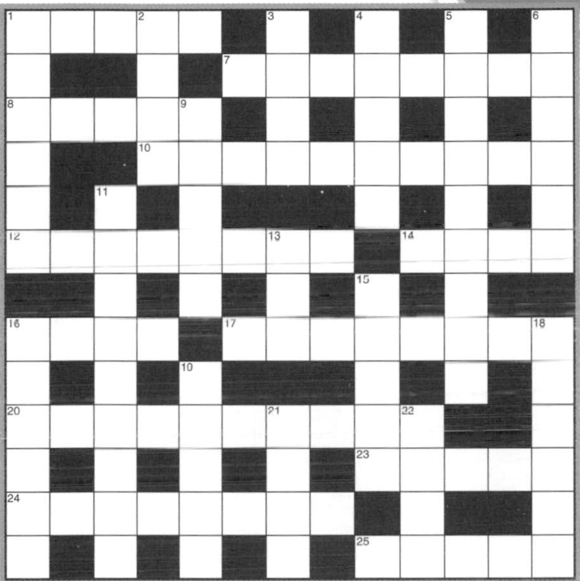

ACROSS

1. Suspect's excuse
7. Enhance
8. Concluding
10. Stringed puppet
12. Insulin-deficient person
14. Footwear item
16. Transmit
17. Twisted (ligament)
20. Without superior
23. Slackened
24. Mercy
25. Crowd brawl

DOWN

1. Meet the cost of
2. Ray of light
3. Tibetan snow beast
4. Severe pain
5. Sewing
6. Cold symptom
9. Oppressed
11. Cares for
13. Small demon
15. Misleading
16. Only
18. Absent-minded scribble
19. Flow-rate recorder
21. Insufficiency
22. Over-gratify

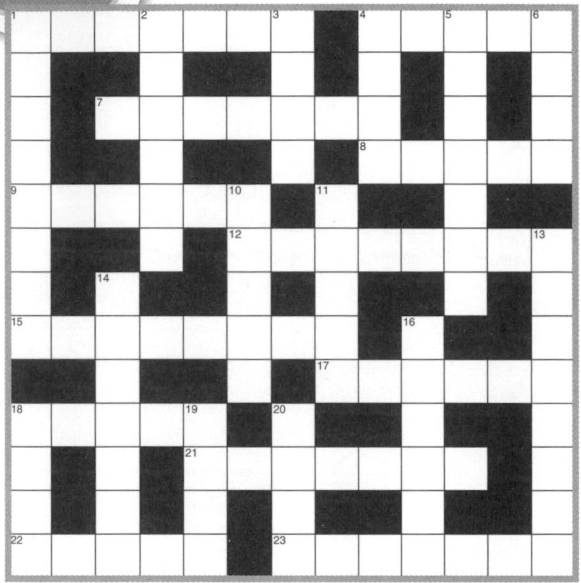

ACROSS

1. Legally kill
4. Emerge (of new chick)
7. Fire from job
8. Detected sound
9. For each, per ...
12. Mimes
15. Submissiveness
17. Shocking ordeal
18. Skewered meat dish
21. Drank
22. Not hollow
23. Survived

DOWN

1. Expulsion of evil spirits
2. Medical rooms
3. Lengthy movie
4. Peace & quiet
5. In direction of
6. Weeded
10. Felt pain
11. Midriff
13. Discarded
14. Women's court sport
16. Tiers
18. Young goats
19. Flying animal
20. Woodwind instrument

ACROSS

1. Small decorative object
5. Male bovine
7. Garden pool
8. Circling (planet)
9. For each one
12. Guided (to seat)
15. Incapacitate
19. Astute
21. Elaborately
22. Peel (apple)
23. Bridge length
24. Tensions

DOWN

1. Bereaved child
2. Confuse
3. Flee to wed
4. Dining surfaces
5. Combat
6. Myth
10. Freezes, ... over
11. Crustacean with nippers
12. Expend, ... up
13. Tall
14. Trick
15. Wilts
16. Reach
17. Coat collar parts
18. Ruminants' mammary glands
19. More devious
20. Boxing-ring surrounds

CROSSWORD 184

ACROSS

1. Supplied funds for
5. Baking chamber
7. Hindu meditation
8. Ran
9. Subtle difference
12. Titled men
15. Printed handout
19. Boats
21. Feasible
22. Frog-like amphibian
23. Length unit
24. Recommends

DOWN

1. The F of UFO
2. Once more
3. Indian class system
4. Tint a deeper shade
5. Possessing
6. Light pushes
10. Saintly radiance
11. Summon
12. Equipment
13. Concept
14. Sudden silence
15. Margin of safety
16. Peeled (of paint)
17. Able to be eaten
18. Stage whispers
19. Submit
20. More appealing

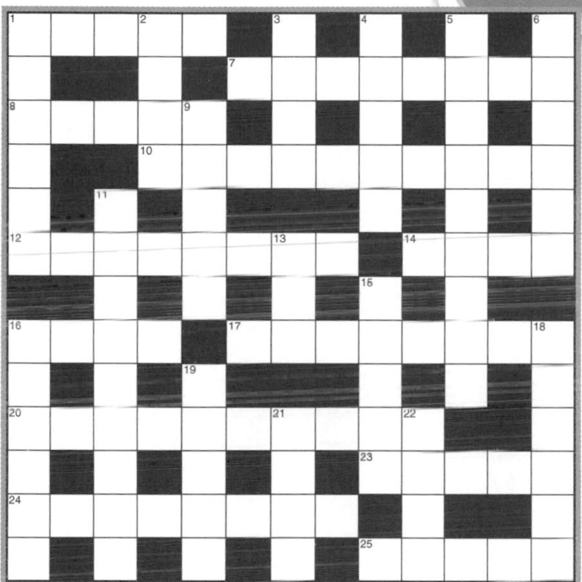

ACROSS

1. Purple shade
7. Long-distance run
8. Song of the Swiss
10. Timepiece repairer
12. Strolls aimlessly
14. Leg joint
16. Touch lips
17. Puts in unsuitable role
20. Embellish
23. Lessened
24. Increased in depth
25. Grate

DOWN

1. Chaos
2. Observe
3. Dusting powder
4. Buddhist fate
5. Unsteadiness
6. Fictitious
9. Nations
11. Sickened
13. Repetitive strain injury (1,1,1)
15. Sharp (pain)
16. Works (dough)
18. Ranked in tennis
19. Leers at
21. Coral shipping hazard
22. Every single

CROSSWORD 186

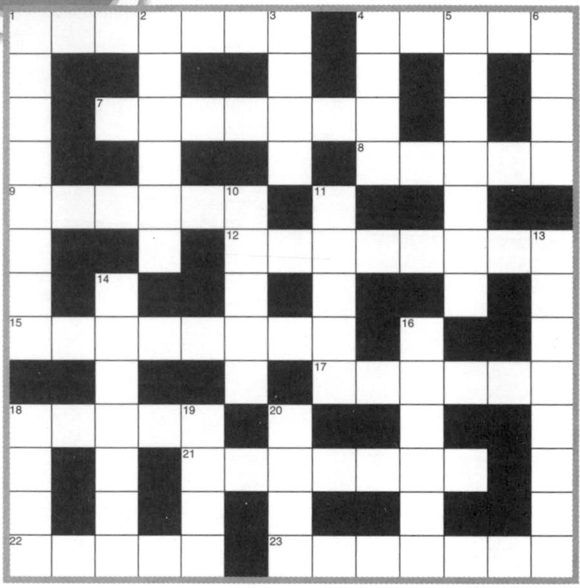

ACROSS

1. Forceful
4. Hair parasite
7. Put in quarantine
8. Playing-card Jack
9. Dog's home
12. Green gems
15. Holder of degree
17. Came close to
18. Relating to speech
21. Castrated men
22. Rail transport
23. Ignited, ... off

DOWN

1. Taking in fluid
2. Missing
3. Informal talk
4. Onion relative
5. Commonly
6. Brink
10. Licit
11. Number of days in a week
13. Followed secretly
14. Eyelash cosmetic
16. Preferably
18. Volcano shaft
19. Trimmed of fat
20. Wildebeests

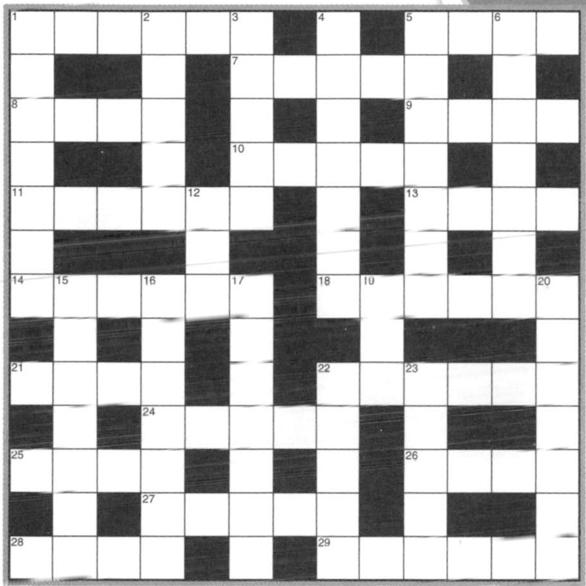

ACROSS

1. Fleet of warships
5. Calf flesh
7. Russian liquor
8. Suspended
9. Beach crustacean
10. Ancient remnant
11. Make hot again
13. Chilled
14. Shins
18. Encouraging cries
21. Matured
22. Radiated
24. Senseless (comment)
25. And
26. Treaty
27. Clock sounds
28. Applications
29. Melted

DOWN

1. Clings (to)
2. Journalistic slant
3. Ward off
4. Poetically scenic
5. Inoculation serum
6. Nonprofessional
12. Inquire
15. Barters
16. Bare-skin enthusiasts
17. Surface wound
19. Garden tool
20. Pacified by medication
22. Creature
23. ..., beta, gamma

CROSSWORD 188

ACROSS

1. One million watts
5. Scientific information
7. Slothful
8. Illegal importer
9. Hexes
12. Craved
15. Gardens
19. Took care of
21. Prescription dispensary
22. Flying frame
23. Desist
24. Balances

DOWN

1. Spitefulness
2. Chasm
3. Donkeys
4. Ruffle (hair)
5. Short pointed knife
6. Reached an understanding
10. Refashion
11. Receive (salary)
12. Certainly
13. Against
14. Necessity
15. Vine fruit
16. Open
17. Hopes
18. Work-shy people
19. Possibly
20. Unclothed

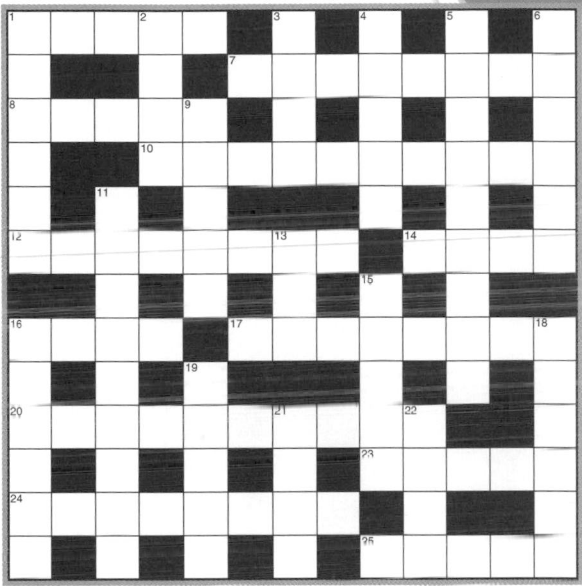

ACROSS

1. Parish minister
7. Game bird
8. Knight's spear
10. Craftsmanship
12. Baking
14. Evil giant
16. Racetrack surface
17. Document fasteners
20. Outlandish
23. Opened mouth wide
24. Orbit
25. Glided on snow

DOWN

1. Coarse
2. Curved doorway
3. Supplied with shoes
4. Trapdoor
5. Lectures loudly
6. US landmark, ... of Liberty
9. This planet
11. Female family head
13. Hard-shelled fruit
15. Imitating
16. Chewy confectionery
18. Squalid
19. Cancel (mission)
21. Pained bark
22. Converse

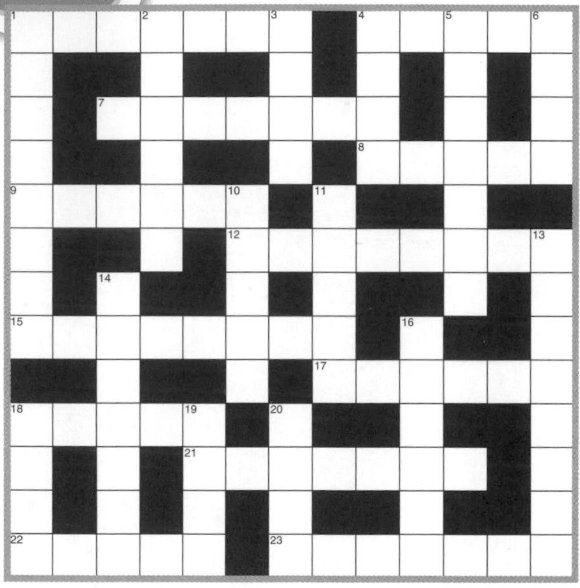

ACROSS

1. Acts as intermediary
4. Numeral
7. Dashed
8. Display rack
9. Folk tale
12. Idle
15. Become stale
17. Deep shock
18. Little crown
21. Exiles
22. Light-rail cars
23. Heaped

DOWN

1. Lacking energy
2. Accustomed
3. Mentioned
4. Fathers
5. Of heredity
6. Petty quarrel
10. Female opera singers
11. Gem side
13. Enlarged
14. Card game
16. Ploy
18. The one there
19. States further
20. Chooses

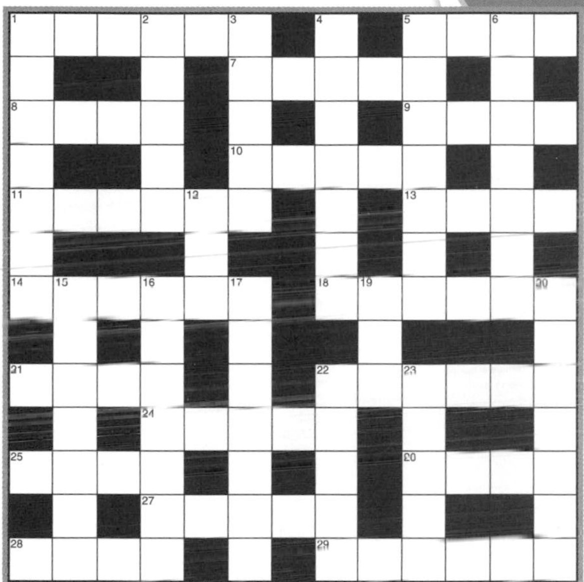

ACROSS

1. More sacred
5. Potter's medium
7. Raise spirits of
8. Immigration permit
9. Science rooms
10. In vain, to no ...
11. Solution
13. Line of rotation
14. Harm
18. Hand in notice
21. Open-mouthed
22. Luggage tags
24. Jewish scholar
25. Half
26. Inner drive
27. Blood-sucking worm
28. Remain
29. First-born

DOWN

1. Hung in air
2. Public profile
3. Baton race
4. Bullfighter
5. Basements
6. Walking slowly
12. Use shovel
15. Supplement
16. Furiously
17. Entitles
19. Historical period
20. Most intrusive
22. Supple
23. Tied up

CROSSWORD 192

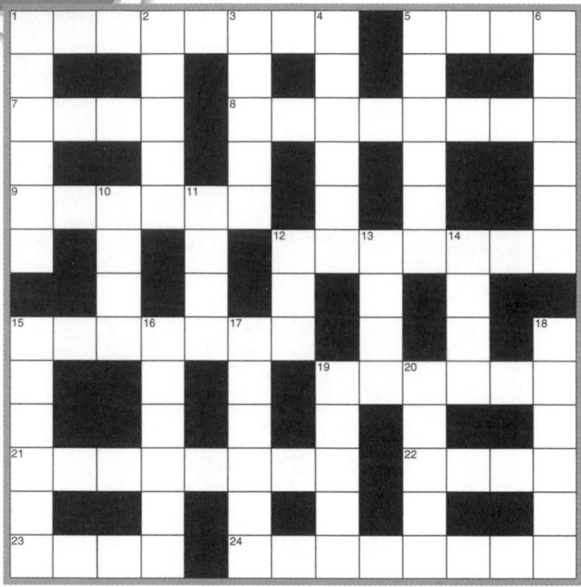

ACROSS

1. Metal container
5. Produced (egg)
7. Minuscule amount
8. Octopus arm
9. Construes
12. Rupturing (muscle)
15. Fragility
19. Drying cloths
21. Numbers
22. Door handle
23. Unchanged, the ...
24. Supervisor

DOWN

1. Film reviewer
2. Cross
3. Ballet dresses
4. Go back on deal
5. Ruler
6. Tinting
10. Hopping parasite
11. Train track
12. Attempt
13. As well
14. Tiny landmass
15. Sides
16. Obstruct
17. Ketchup, ... sauce
18. Weather map line
19. Oral sense
20. Rouses

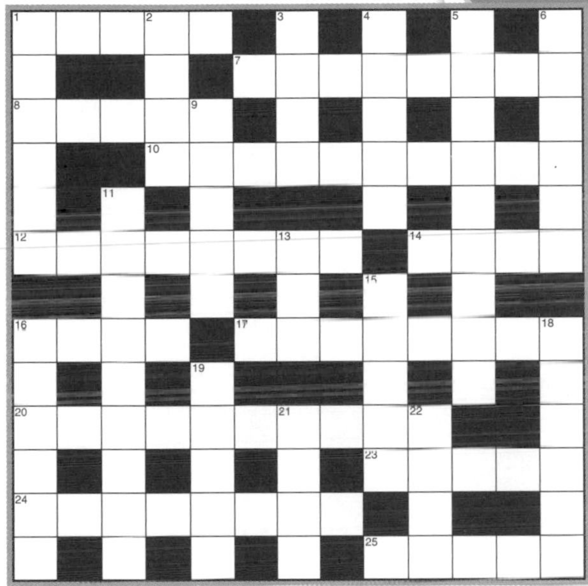

ACROSS

1. In front
7. Attacked suddenly
8. Illustrious
10. Lurching
12. Most fortunate
14. Wanes
16. Of the mouth
17. In work
20. Underwater vessels
23. Recorded (music)
24. Style
25. Straighten

DOWN

1. Once-a-year
2. Troubles
3. Self-satisfied
4. Sri Lankan money unit
5. Church singers
6. Wise sayings
9. Moral standard
11. Clambered
13. Arithmetic problem
15. Frozen rain
16. Shellfish
18. Benumb
19. Lethal
21. Measure of length
22. Yacht canvas

CROSSWORD 194

ACROSS

1. Sending forth
4. Tasteless (food)
7. Antiquated
8. Australian marsupial
9. Embark, get ...
12. By surprise
15. Rescued disaster victims
17. Citrus fruit
18. Supporting beam
21. 100-cent units
22. Quarry detonation
23. Set up (tent)

DOWN

1. Example
2. Commotion
3. Snatch
4. Reverse
5. Matters
6. Information
10. Deceives
11. Lariat
13. Compressed
14. Mosquito fever
16. Cloth
18. Grenade
19. Rewrite
20. Collapse wearily

ACROSS

1. Tile-chip picture
5. Back of foot
7. Peru beast
8. Arched roof
9. Commend (for bravery)
10. Fissure
11. Decreased in size
13. Night sky object
14. Pulled sharply
18. Most depressed
21. Domestic poultry
22. Hoisted
24. Dog lead
25. Broad
26. Field entrance
27. Mountain range top
28. Serpents
29. Church podium

DOWN

1. Demureness
2. Stadium
3. Snap (fingers)
4. Sunshade
5. Metal-cutting blade
6. Ensnares
12. Born as
15. Great pains
16. Assassins
17. Insists
19. Rowing aid
20. Neatest
22. Chick's call
23. Cherub

CROSSWORD 196

ACROSS

1. Fracture
5. Scream
7. Incendiary device
8. Ambled
9. Build up
12. Fought rowdily
15. Cooks in juices
19. Martial art
21. Whitened
22. Metropolis
23. Long narrative
24. Shame

DOWN

1. North American feline
2. Fossil resin
3. Supermarket lane
4. Spookier
5. Rainbow hue
6. Wedged
10. Unconscious state
11. Large jars
12. Public transport
13. Opera song
14. Volcanic matter
15. Financial inducements
16. Galapagos lizard
17. Engraved
18. Rewrite on machine
19. Prestige
20. Crop up again

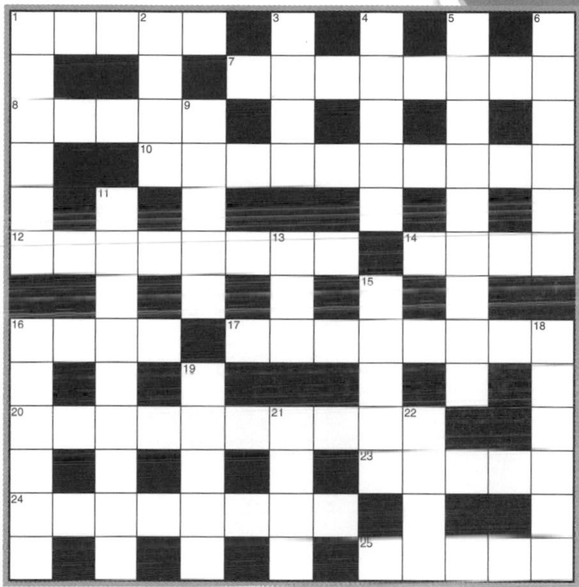

ACROSS

1. Regard smugly
7. Dig
8. Planet's path
10. Gazettes
12. Dough ball
14. A long way off
16. Large jug
17. Fiddled (with thumbs)
20. Item owned
23. Valletta is there
24. Seedless raisins
25. Seasonal weather pattern

DOWN

1. Gleamed
2. Similar
3. Cancels (TV show)
4. Light summer dish
5. Cataract
6. Smaller
9. Relates
11. Hugely
13. Currently
15. Colloquial turn of phrase
16. Uncover
18. Ten years
19. Kidney treatment, ... dialysis
21. Place to sit
22. Armed fleet

CROSSWORD 198

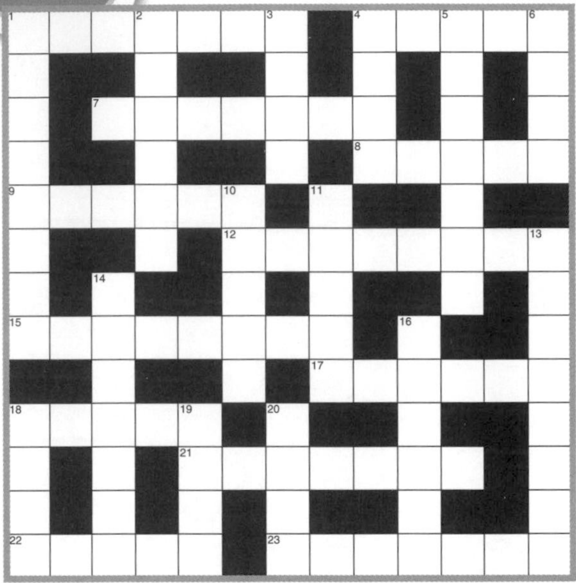

ACROSS

1. Sighing sleepily
4. Acted wordlessly
7. Plush
8. Artist's stand
9. Me
12. Brave
15. Rush headlong (of herd)
17. Thundered
18. Skin-diving gear
21. Infectious viral disease
22. Water lily
23. Northern sea fish

DOWN

1. Face veils
2. Niece & ...
3. Clarified butter
4. Breed (with)
5. Car race official
6. Dress-up toy
10. Blends by melting
11. Bread maker
13. Loitering
14. Most indistinct
16. Profession
18. Dirt
19. Sound boosters
20. Whip stroke

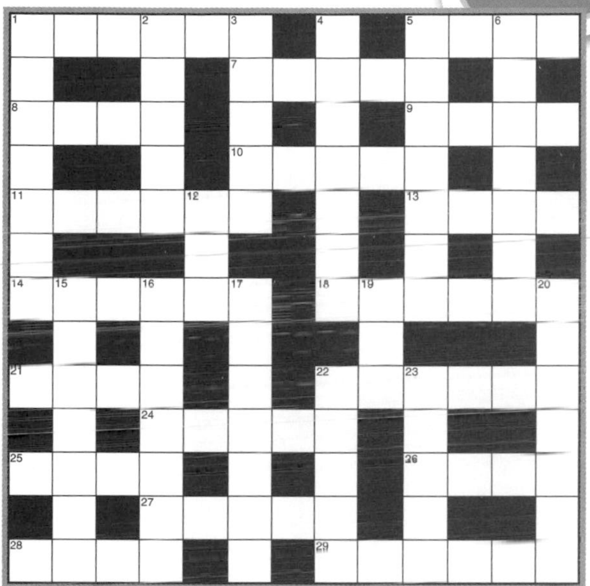

ACROSS

1. Decided
5. Wounded
7. Male relative
8. Great Bear constellation, ... Major
9. Horizontal
10. Barely sufficient
11. For each one
13. Golf club
14. Carnivores, meat ...
18. Stroke lovingly
21. Shapeless mass
22. IOU signatory
24. Banded quartz
25. Pairs
26. Revolve
27. Move crab-wise
28. Curl (of smoke)
29. Hardly ever

DOWN

1. Campaign for cause
2. Slide on ice
3. Hospital worker
4. Of the Pacific or Atlantic
5. More weighty
6. Motivations
12. Motor vehicle
15. Permitted
16. Ambassador's residence
17. Threads
19. Alcoholic brew
20. Elastic
22. Adjourn to a future date
23. Mongolian capital, Ulan ...

ACROSS

1. Without sound
5. Anchor (boat)
7. Grand-scale
8. Fell to pieces
9. Biblical prayers
12. Rises
15. Looser
19. Halts
21. Luxuriously self-indulgent
22. Gambling cubes
23. Symbol of peace
24. Snakes

DOWN

1. Hibernates
2. Do well (at)
3. Sewn folds
4. Teenagers
5. Movable
6. Half-diameter
10. Greenish-blue
11. Perfume ingredient
12. House cooler, ... conditioner
13. Manage
14. Pen tips
15. Screened from sun
16. Bring into existence
17. Forces out
18. Resources
19. Supply food
20. Confuse

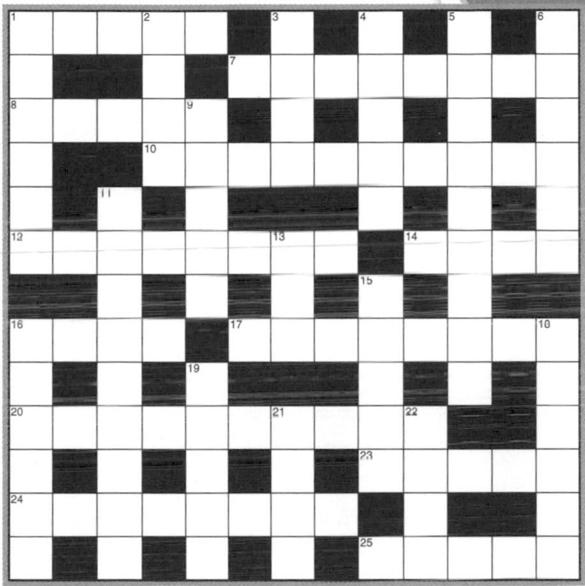

ACROSS

1. Staple crop
7. Habituate
8. Agricultural
10. Horseracing track
12. Action-packed
14. Curved-bill bird
16. Apparel
17. Spiritually raised
20. Aroused again
23. Titled
24. Intestines
25. Nutmeg or paprika

DOWN

1. Fended (off)
2. A bit open
3. Area measurement
4. Trial panel member
5. Distinctive feature
6. Inserts firmly
9. Tibetan monks
11. Cloudy eye condition
13. Mischievous sprite
15. Animate
16. Semiprecious stone
18. Absent-minded drawing
19. Festive occasions
21. Congers
22. Moist

CROSSWORD 202

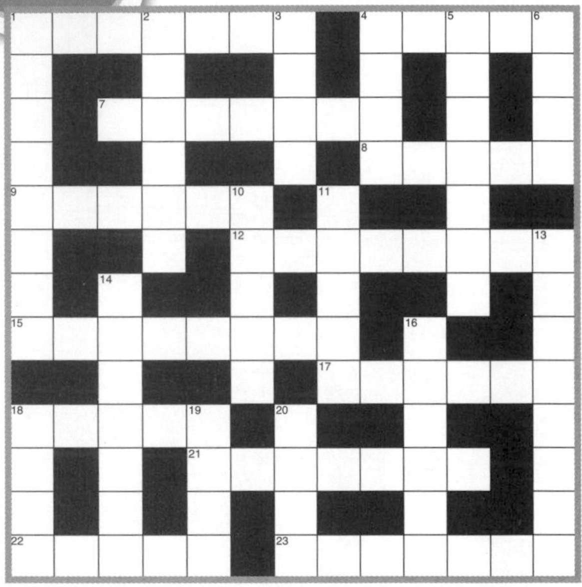

ACROSS

1. Sparked
4. Attain
7. Mouse noises
8. Aptitude
9. Propose
12. Be visible once more
15. Seepages
17. Intercepted, ... off
18. Domain
21. Without weapons
22. Religious splinter groups
23. Gestured with finger

DOWN

1. Carnival
2. Follow-up book
3. University faculty head
4. Danger
5. Shopping walkways
6. Large piece
10. Coffee sediment
11. Stringent
13. Blushed
14. Extremist
16. Underground hollow
18. Engine turns
19. Earthenware cups
20. Table light

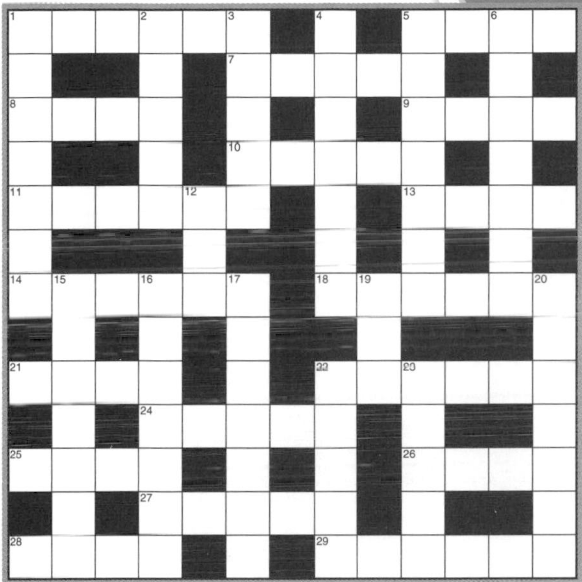

ACROSS

1. Unoccupied
5. Felines
7. Become liable for
8. Supporting beam
9. Regrettably
10. Brings up (child)
11. Corresponds to
13. Take notice of
14. Barbaric
18. Made home in tree
21. Lyrical poems
22. Marine animal, sea ...
24. Cultural symbols
25. Air pollution
26. Tumble
27. Wall recess
28. Tiny insects
29. Harvested

DOWN

1. Receptacles
2. Major blood vessel
3. Cake layers
4. Eight-sided figure
5. Collisions
6. Circus swing
12. Chair part
15. Stomach
16. Appoints
17. Compel compliance with
19. Make mistake
20. Hung freely
22. Escort
23. Roughly (that date)

CROSSWORD 204

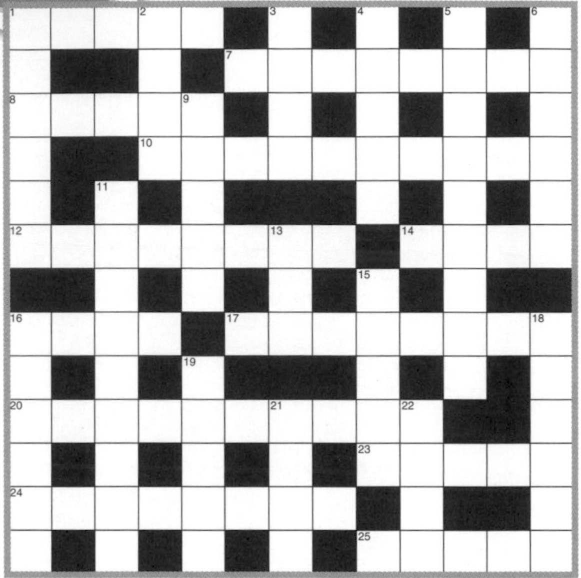

ACROSS

1. Inexpensive
7. More gluttonous
8. Hickory tree nut
10. Juveniles
12. Ousting from power
14. Untruthful person
16. Cover up
17. Moved forward
20. Attacking with missiles
23. Spun threads
24. Indiscreet
25. Morbid spectator

DOWN

1. Duplicated
2. Off
3. Tiny songbird
4. Minimum amount
5. Clock
6. Pencil-mark remover
9. Loud
11. Widespread diseases
13. Non-verbal yes
15. Wet (weather)
16. Routines
18. Medieval maiden
19. Sorrowfully
21. Dry earth
22. Deep wound

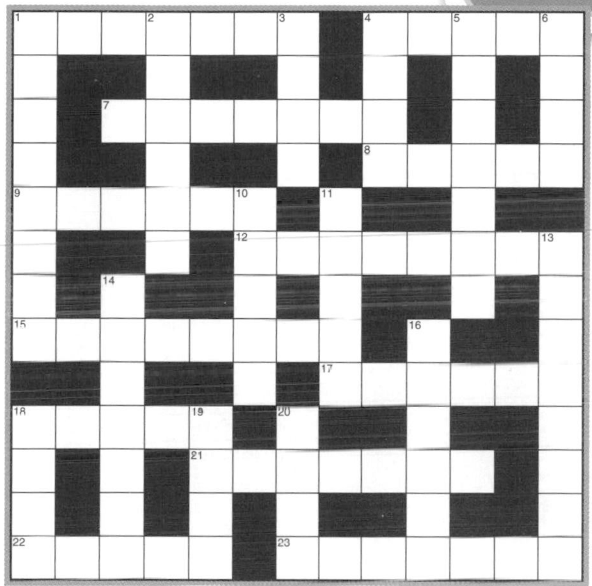

ACROSS

1. Glowed
4. Measuring device
7. Hustles
8. Position
9. Oily
12. Instances
15. Daughter's child
17. Radio interference
18. Interlace on loom
21. Suitability
22. Resident
23. Incapacitate

DOWN

1. Resenting
2. Without scruples
3. Aromatic herb
4. Pant
5. Normally
6. Loosen
10. Fermenting agent
11. Young deer
13. Fort
14. Diabolic
16. Queasiness
18. Room division
19. Fragrant tea, ... Grey
20. Horse farm

CROSSWORD 206

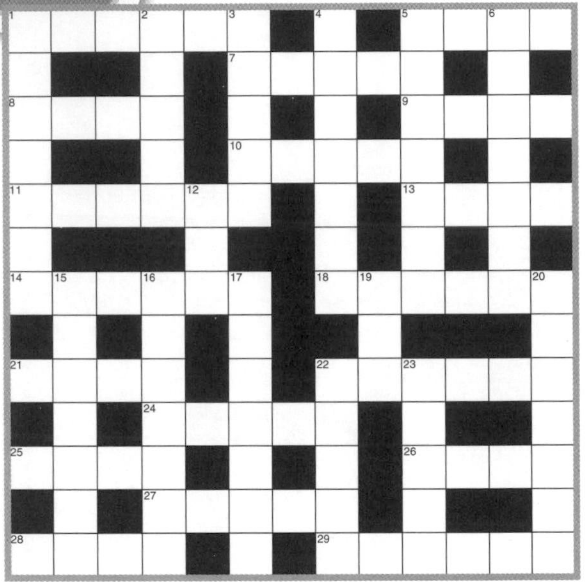

ACROSS

1. Inborn
5. Cajole
7. Mutineer
8. Mortuary table
9. Nervous
10. Greek letter
11. Despise
13. Steals from
14. Italian sausage
18. Of medicinal plants
21. Burial vault
22. Lyrics
24. Frostily
25. Put in the ground (of seeds)
26. Cow flesh
27. Body part
28. Requests, ... for
29. Affable

DOWN

1. Disparaging remarks
2. Monastery superior
3. Wear away
4. Put an end to (law)
5. More distinct
6. Branch of mathematics
12. Smoked pork
15. Loving
16. Pure white animals
17. Encroach
19. The self
20. Lecherous
22. Competing
23. Ocean liner bedroom

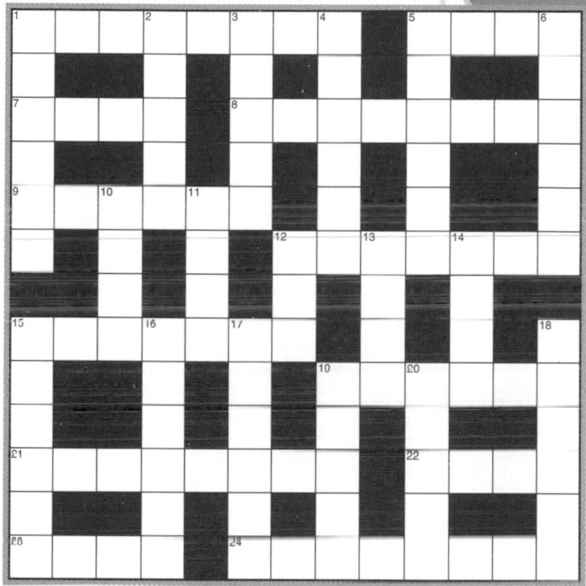

ACROSS

1. Not dangerous
5. Tofu bean
7. Broad smile
8. Venomous-tailed creature
9. Leaseholder
12. Sickness
15. Hurried (glance)
19. Consequence
21. Acquainted (with)
22. Paint roughly
23. Father (children)
24. Anticipation

DOWN

1. Immensely
2. Money factories
3. Follow on
4. Garden tool
5. Drain off
6. Cancels
10. Glide aloft
11. Reflected sound
12. Climbing vine
13. Bread section
14. Otherwise
15. Precipices
16. Salt solution
17. Broadcast receivers
18. Horse shed
19. Gains
20. Soft toffee

CROSSWORD 208

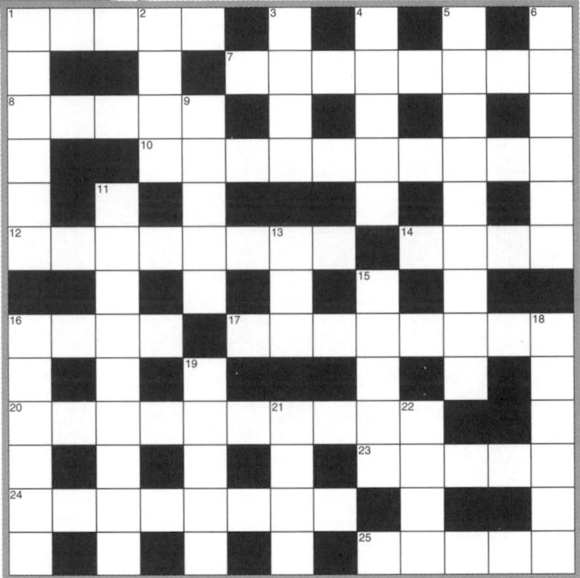

ACROSS

1. Native New Zealander
7. Breathing out
8. Doorposts
10. Business venture
12. Mariner
14. The one here
16. Rain heavily
17. Power generating machines
20. Rituals
23. Sailing boat
24. Confection on a stick
25. Meat jelly

DOWN

1. Army officers
2. Gown
3. Wheel spindle
4. Coarse files
5. Completing
6. Reaches an understanding
9. Move furtively
11. Unaffectedly
13. Large bird
15. Hard black wood
16. Flower parts
18. Infected
19. Furious
21. Cult hero
22. Depletes

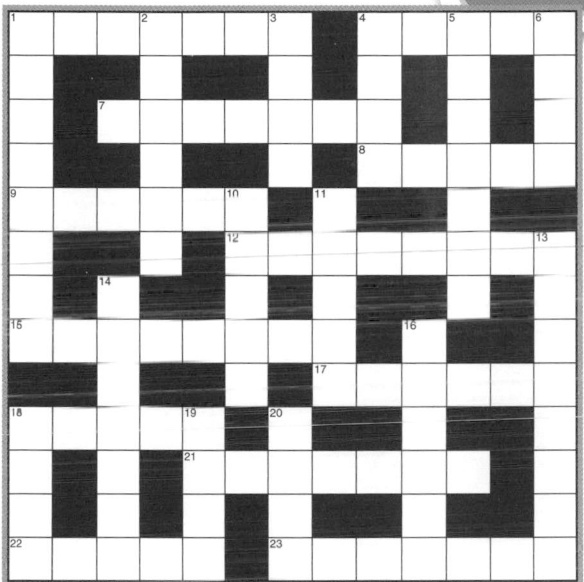

ACROSS

1. Most cherished (memories)
4. Weight measure
7. Edible leafstalk
8. Trap
9. Dribble
12. Rain shield
15. Sword holder
17. Ample
18. Denim trousers
21. Animal hide material
22. Ruled (paper)
23. Garbed

DOWN

1. Predicts
2. Mexican flower
3. In comparison to
4. Spheres
5. Remarkable
6. Fencing blade
10. Of the ear
11. Tolerate
13. Moored (of ship)
14. Model of excellence
16. Cringes
18. Prison
19. Skidded
20. Dole (out)

CROSSWORD 210

ACROSS

1. Inuit canoes
5. Bearded animal
7. Lazy person
8. Temperament
9. Australian gemstone
10. School tests
11. Tends (patients)
13. Detergent foam
14. African wildlife tour
18. Four-door cars
21. Payment for goods
22. Articulated
24. Elude (capture)
25. Beloved
26. Alliance
27. More senior
28. Accustomed (to)
29. Pouted

DOWN

1. Japanese robes
2. South American mountain range
3. Dimensions
4. False names
5. Earned before tax
6. Desert
12. Listening organ
15. Emerges from sleep
16. Stuck (to)
17. Entrails
19. Self-pride
20. Pacified by medication
22. Turns suddenly
23. Incite to action

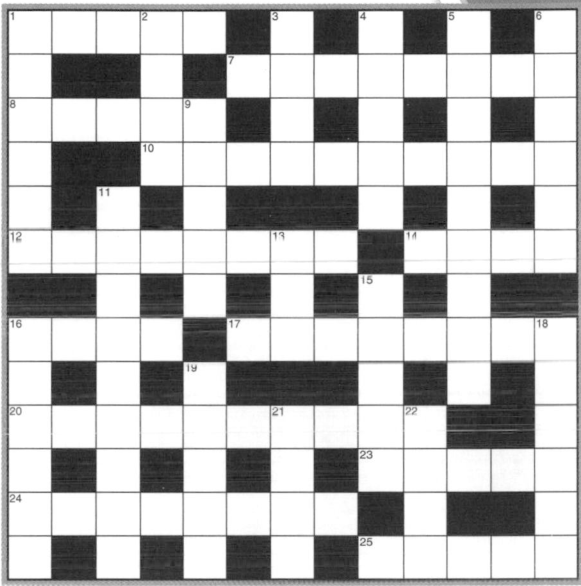

ACROSS

1. Book of maps
7. Speechmakers
8. From the time that
10. Very tall building
12. Lately
14. Brief calm
16. Quantity of paper
17. Deeply shocked
20. Evil conduct
23. Chaos
24. Most in want
25. Slalom competitor

DOWN

1. Reply
2. Circle curves
3. Therapeutic baths
4. Unite in matrimony
5. Usefully
6. Celestial
9. Just managing, ... out a living
11. Superficial cuts
13. Remove branches from
15. Low wetland
16. Using oars
18. Ballerina
19. Be appropriate to
21. Plane tip
22. Became submerged

CROSSWORD 212

ACROSS

1. Clap
4. Slow-moving mammal
7. Able to be read
8. Get to feet
9. Sewing cotton
12. Studied closely
15. Leave place of danger
17. Harvester
18. Taunt
21. Quantities
22. Splashes (through)
23. Yapping in pain

DOWN

1. Aircraft height
2. Looked sneeringly
3. Sponges lightly
4. Witnesses
5. Gains possession of
6. Head covering
10. Time lag
11. More secure
13. Towering over
14. Marched in procession
16. Portable computer
18. Defrost
19. Grain tips
20. Small bunch of flowers

ACROSS

1. Respect, ... highly
5. Loosen (buttons)
7. Accurate
8. Bass brass instrument
9. Freezes, ... over
10. Period on guard
11. Puzzling question
13. Object
14. Embezzled
18. Coyest
21. Uterus
22. Beverage vessel
24. Sun-powered energy
25. Make with wool
26. Fish breathing organ
27. Student's written assignment
28. Bell-shaped fruit
29. Scatter

DOWN

1. Withdraws (from contest)
2. Grant
3. Dig
4. Places aimed for
5. Public service
6. Intensifies
12. Untruth
15. Defeat soundly
16. Food crustacean
17. Most dignified
19. Shade
20. Fallen
22. Serving platters
23. Enrage

CROSSWORD 214

ACROSS

1. Went aboard ship
5. Had to repay
7. On an occasion
8. Tidiness
9. Greatly pleases
12. Makes beloved
15. Temper outburst
19. Did penance (for)
21. Living being
22. Woodwind instrument
23. Tropical tuber
24. Goes back over (path)

DOWN

1. Summoned up
2. Skilled
3. Monarchs
4. Fire-breathing monster
5. Elaborately embellished
6. Dance clubs
10. Nameless author
11. At all times
12. Deciduous tree
13. Soil
14. Yemen port
15. Gullet
16. Red salad fruit
17. Less attractive
18. Ruminants' mammary glands
19. Let in
20. Atmosphere layer

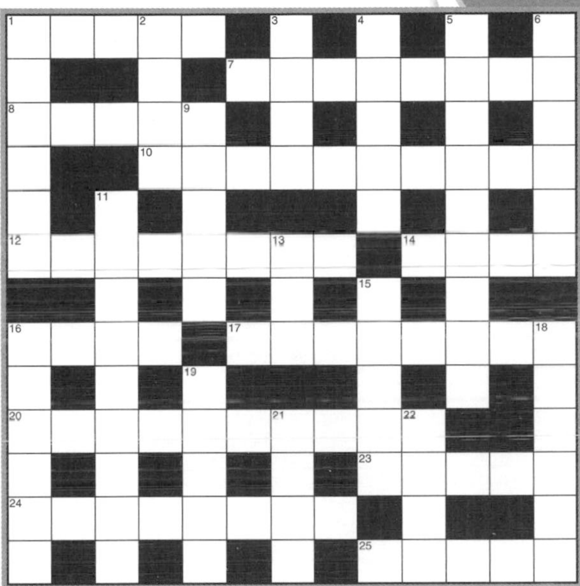

ACROSS

1. Spend time idly
7. Chilliness
8. Fatality
10. Last golf hole
12. Overpowered by sound
14. Fervent request
16. Fault
17. Fixated
20. Milk-jelly dessert
23. Predatory bird
24. Originates (from)
25. Wrote on keyboard

DOWN

1. Having raised lines
2. Poker stake
3. Butterfly relative
4. Pastes
5. Bankrupt
6. Respiratory ailment
9. Trekked
11. Twin-hulled boat
13. Fluctuation, ... and flow
15. Meet & join
16. Legendary tales
18. Speak up for
19. Remnant
21. Tip of triangle
22. Effortless

CROSSWORD 216

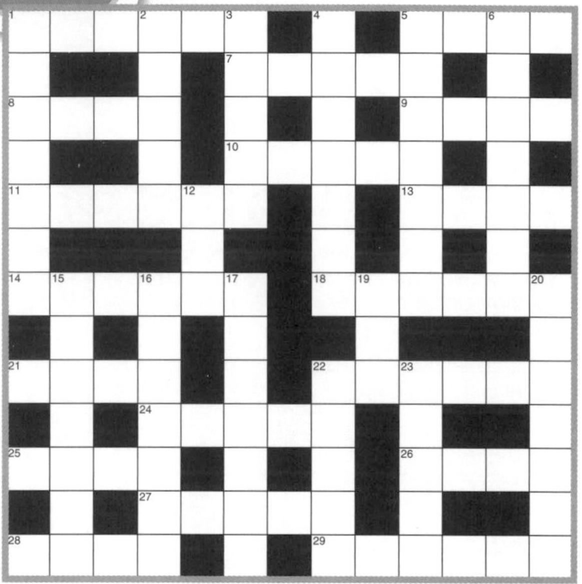

ACROSS

1. Woman
5. Oxen harness
7. In which place?
8. Misplaced
9. Unavailability
10. Majestic
11. Mass departure
13. Overlook
14. Skill
18. Pattern
21. Power of refusal
22. Womb
24. Use dragnet
25. Prepare for take-off
26. Radio knob
27. Happen
28. Spotted
29. Every time

DOWN

1. Utmost (confidence)
2. Performed
3. Pitchers
4. Pretended
5. Golden hues
6. Striking with foot
12. Grecian pot
15. Standard
16. Feeling
17. Nicotine plant
19. Consume
20. Lies snugly
22. Extremist
23. Bequeath

ACROSS

1. Movable dwellings
5. Give up
7. Sicilian volcano
8. Boldly decorate
9. Disgraced
12. Plume
15. Small axe
19. Roved
21. Droopiness
22. Completed
23. Palm fruit
24. Tactful

DOWN

1. Dairy product
2. Burglary warning
3. Alter (rules)
4. Pacify
5. Charmingly old-fashioned
6. Oil ship
10. Border on
11. Engrave
12. Suitable
13. Type of saxophone
14. Damage
15. Cried (of wolf)
16. Twosome
17. Go beyond
18. Most peculiar
19. Pauses
20. Snake, death ...

CROSSWORD 218

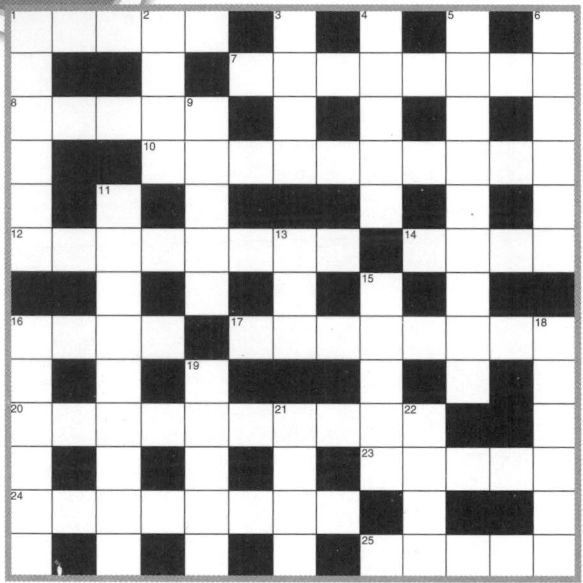

ACROSS

1. Nobody (2-3)
7. Catching fire
8. Step (on)
10. Demotion
12. Circle width
14. Henhouse produce
16. Young goats
17. Computer accessory
20. Eliminated
23. Steam-room
24. Passenger lift
25. Magazine edition

DOWN

1. Snared
2. Within range
3. Leer
4. Mauve flower
5. Fluent in two languages
6. Spies, secret ...
9. Dissuade
11. Abrasive sheet
13. Before (poetic)
15. Woodwind instruments
16. Zoo custodian
18. Bestow as a gift
19. Temporary visitor documents
21. At summit of
22. Speaker's platform

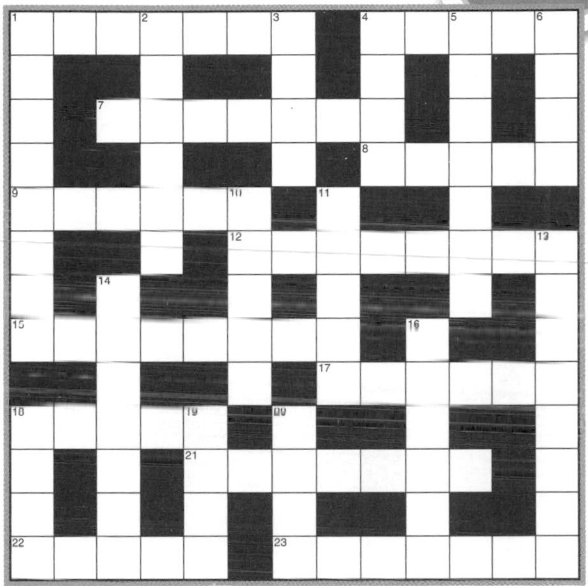

ACROSS

1. Nauseous on boat
4. Nourishes
7. Thin timber board
8. Avid
9. Buccaneer
12. Overjoyed
15. Mirrors
17. Tooth coating
18. Small fenced-in areas
21. Ignorant
22. Located
23. Marauding

DOWN

1. Stone-carving artist
2. Turkish ruler
3. Understand
4. Become dim
5. Puzzles
6. Tart
10. Throw out
11. Maltreat
13. Adding up (scores)
14. Personal insult
16. Spoiled
18. Starchy tubers
19. Prosecuted
20. Wolf home

CROSSWORD 220

ACROSS

1. Doctor's ward visits
5. Mar
7. Rub until sore
8. Brief letter
9. Periods
10. Of birth
11. Anticipate
13. Pigmented eye membrane
14. Crockery item
18. Tattered
21. Camel's mound
22. Moves sinuously
24. Indoor game, ... tennis
25. Grain store
26. Cougar
27. Quick wash
28. Gets on in years
29. Speckled

DOWN

1. Sprinters
2. Sister's girl
3. Flower smell
4. More distant
5. Staggering
6. Dream
12. Snooker stick
15. Entertaining
16. Hostage-takers
17. Sashes
19. Afflict
20. Break up (group)
22. Stitched
23. Computer data

SOLUTIONS

1

U	N	D	U	L	Y	■	C	■	B	L	U	E
K	■	■	S	■	A	B	A	S	E	■	R	■
U	L	N	A	■	C	■	R	■	D	E	A	F
L	■	■	G	■	H	O	A	R	D	■	N	■
E	F	F	E	C	T	■	M	■	I	B	I	S
L	■	■	■	A	■	■	E	■	N	■	U	■
E	A	T	E	R	S	■	L	E	G	U	M	E
■	I	■	C	■	C	■	■	K	■	■	■	N
O	R	A	L	■	R	■	C	E	D	I	N	G
■	S	■	I	M	A	G	E	■	O	■	■	U
C	H	I	P	■	T	■	A	■	P	O	L	L
■	I	■	S	O	C	K	S	■	E	■	■	F
E	P	E	E	■	H	■	E	N	D	O	W	S

2

V	I	R	T	U	O	U	S	■	T	U	N	A
E	■	■	A	■	M	■	H	■	E	■	■	M
N	U	M	B	■	I	N	A	C	T	I	V	E
D	■	■	I	■	T	■	D	■	H	■	■	N
O	R	D	E	R	S	■	U	■	E	■	■	D
R	■	I	■	O	■	S	W	E	R	V	E	S
■	■	M	■	A	■	A	■	A	■	A	■	■
G	A	S	T	R	I	C	■	S	■	N	■	B
A	■	■	R	■	D	■	C	E	L	E	R	Y
S	■	■	U	■	L	■	R	■	O	■	■	P
H	U	M	A	N	E	L	Y	■	C	O	M	A
E	■	■	N	■	R	■	P	■	A	■	■	S
S	E	C	T	■	S	E	T	T	L	E	R	S

3

M	E	T	A	L	■	S	■	T	■	R	■	A
A	■	■	P	■	S	P	E	A	K	E	R	S
J	E	W	E	L	■	E	■	K	■	I	■	I
O	■	■	D	A	Y	D	R	E	A	M	E	D
R	■	C	■	M	■	■	■	N	■	B	■	E
S	H	A	M	B	L	E	S	■	S	U	D	S
■	■	T	■	S	■	E	■	S	■	R	■	■
E	R	A	S	■	C	L	E	A	N	S	E	D
F	■	M	■	A	■	■	■	U	■	E	■	A
F	L	A	M	B	O	Y	A	N	T	■	■	W
O	■	R	■	Y	■	A	■	A	H	E	A	D
R	E	A	S	S	E	R	T	■	U	■	■	L
T	■	N	■	S	■	N	■	A	G	I	L	E

4

D	E	B	A	S	E	D	■	P	E	A	R	S
E	■	■	M	■	■	E	■	O	■	Q	■	U
A	■	O	B	L	O	N	G	S	■	U	■	E
D	■	■	L	■	■	S	■	Y	E	A	R	S
L	E	G	E	N	D	■	E	■	■	T	■	■
O	■	■	D	■	I	M	B	I	B	I	N	G
C	■	S	■	■	V	■	B	■	■	C	■	U
K	E	E	P	S	A	K	E	■	C	■	■	I
■	■	T	■	■	N	■	D	R	A	P	E	D
N	O	B	L	E	■	L	■	■	M	■	■	A
U	■	A	■	R	E	A	C	T	E	D	■	N
L	■	C	■	R	■	U	■	■	R	■	■	C
L	A	K	E	S	■	D	I	S	A	B	L	E

5

B	A	N	A	N	A	■	A	■	H	E	A	P
E	■	■	S	■	V	O	D	K	A	■	D	■
W	A	S	H	■	O	■	V	■	M	O	A	T
A	■	■	E	■	I	T	E	M	S	■	M	■
I	R	O	N	E	D	■	R	■	T	E	A	T
L	■	■	■	N	■	■	B	■	E	■	N	■
S	A	L	A	D	S	■	S	P	R	I	T	E
■	P	■	R	■	T	■	■	I	■	■	■	Y
E	P	I	C	■	R	■	D	E	C	O	D	E
■	R	■	A	M	A	Z	E	■	Y	■	■	L
P	O	N	D	■	N	■	C	■	C	O	P	E
■	V	■	E	L	D	E	R	■	L	■	■	T
K	E	G	S	■	S	■	Y	I	E	L	D	S

6

7

P	A	N	E	L	■	R	■	V	■	H	■	H
O	■	■	M	■	H	U	M	I	D	I	T	Y
T	U	T	U	S	■	M	■	S	■	N	■	B
E	■	■	S	T	E	P	L	A	D	D	E	R
N	■	R	■	O	■	■	■	S	■	S	■	I
T	H	A	T	C	H	E	S	■	D	I	E	D
■	■	I	■	K	■	A	■	L	■	G	■	■
S	U	N	K	■	P	R	E	A	C	H	E	R
A	■	W	■	M	■	■	■	N	■	T	■	A
T	R	A	D	E	M	A	R	K	S	■	■	I
I	■	T	■	N	■	B	■	Y	E	L	P	S
R	U	E	F	U	L	L	Y	■	E	■	■	E
E	■	R	■	S	■	Y	■	S	K	I	E	D

8

T	I	G	H	T	E	R	■	T	I	A	R	A
A	■	■	O	■	■	E	■	I	■	L	■	R
M	■	I	S	O	L	A	T	E	■	M	■	C
P	■	■	I	■	■	D	■	R	E	A	C	H
E	T	H	N	I	C	■	F	■	■	N	■	■
R	■	■	G	■	E	V	A	L	U	A	T	E
E	■	I	■	■	D	■	X	■	■	C	■	D
D	O	M	I	N	A	T	E	■	T	■	■	U
■	■	P	■	■	R	■	S	T	A	T	I	C
T	W	A	N	G	■	A	■	■	C	■	■	A
A	■	L	■	A	F	F	E	C	T	S	■	T
U	■	E	■	P	■	A	■	■	I	■	■	O
T	I	D	E	S	■	R	E	S	C	U	E	R

9

13

S	E	D	A	T	E	■	M	■	B	O	D	E
E	■	■	W	■	Q	U	A	K	E	■	A	■
C	U	B	A	■	U	■	L	■	S	A	I	L
T	■	■	K	■	A	B	A	T	E	■	R	■
O	R	D	E	A	L	■	R	■	E	D	I	T
R	■	■	■	I	■	■	I	■	C	■	E	■
S	A	F	A	R	I	■	A	G	H	A	S	T
■	I	■	N	■	G	■	■	E	■	■	■	I
C	R	U	X	■	U	■	F	L	A	Y	E	D
■	L	■	I	N	A	N	E	■	R	■	■	I
W	I	P	E	■	N	■	L	■	C	A	K	E
■	N	■	T	R	A	W	L	■	E	■	■	S
R	E	L	Y	■	S	■	S	A	D	I	S	T

10

14

Y	U	L	E	T	I	D	E	■	N	E	S	T
A	■	■	V	■	M	■	N	■	U	■	■	A
N	O	N	E	■	P	E	A	S	A	N	T	S
K	■	■	N	■	L	■	M	■	N	■	■	S
E	A	R	T	H	Y	■	E	■	C	■	■	E
D	■	I	■	E	■	G	L	E	E	F	U	L
■	■	N	■	A	■	O	■	D	■	A	■	■
R	I	D	D	L	E	D	■	G	■	S	■	C
A	■	■	O	■	N	■	N	E	C	T	A	R
F	■	■	L	■	M	■	A	■	I	■	■	E
F	O	U	L	N	E	S	S	■	T	O	G	A
I	■	■	O	■	S	■	A	■	E	■	■	M
A	T	O	P	■	H	O	L	I	D	A	Y	S

11

15

A	S	H	A	M	E	D	■	C	A	G	E	D
S	■	■	L	■	R	■	A	■	O	■	■	U
S	■	F	A	C	T	U	A	L	■	R	■	E
E	■	■	R	■	■	M	■	F	E	I	N	T
M	A	I	M	E	D	■	V	■	■	L	■	■
B	■	■	S	■	E	M	E	R	A	L	D	S
L	■	C	■	■	B	■	X	■	■	A	■	Y
E	V	A	C	U	A	T	E	■	B	■	■	N
■	■	N	■	■	R	■	S	C	A	L	E	D
C	H	A	F	F	■	L	■	■	R	■	■	R
H	■	S	■	L	E	I	S	U	R	E	■	O
I	■	T	■	U	■	M	■	■	E	■	■	M
C	R	A	N	E	■	B	O	N	D	A	G	E

12

16

P	O	T	A	T	O	■	H	■	H	E	A	T
I	■	■	R	■	C	R	A	Z	Y	■	B	■
N	O	D	E	■	C	■	T	■	D	U	A	L
B	■	■	N	■	U	L	C	E	R	■	N	■
A	F	F	A	I	R	■	H	■	A	D	D	S
L	■	■	■	C	■	■	E	■	N	■	O	■
L	A	D	L	E	D	■	S	I	T	I	N	G
■	N	■	E	■	E	■	■	R	■	■	■	A
A	G	E	D	■	C	■	F	E	A	S	T	S
■	E	■	G	U	A	V	A	■	R	■	■	K
T	R	U	E	■	Y	■	L	■	O	N	C	E
■	E	■	R	E	E	F	S	■	M	■	■	T
O	D	D	S	■	D	■	E	V	A	D	E	S

SOLUTIONS

17

C	O	M	M	A	N	D	S		J	A	D	E
O			A		U		K		E			X
S	U	M	P		D	I	A	B	E	T	I	C
M			L		E		T		R			E
O	T	H	E	R	S		E		E			E
S		U		I		B	R	I	D	G	E	D
		L		S		I		O		A		
B	L	A	C	K	E	N		N		L		R
R			O		X		E	S	C	A	P	E
E			B		P		W		A			M
E	X	C	A	V	A	T	E		P	U	M	A
Z			L		N		D		E			N
E	A	S	T		D	E	S	E	R	T	E	D

18

I	N	V	A	D	E	D		M	E	T	A	L
N			T			E		O		R		I
T		S	T	E	W	A	R	D		E		V
I			A			N		E	L	A	T	E
M	A	R	I	N	A		R			D		
A			N		U	S	E	F	U	L	L	Y
T		A			N		E			E		A
E	S	C	O	R	T	E	D		D			S
		I			S		S	N	A	T	C	H
N	U	D	G	E		A			W			M
O		I		N	A	B	B	I	N	G		A
D		T		V		E			E			K
S	H	Y	L	Y		T	R	U	D	G	E	S

19

L	A	S	T	L	Y		C		T	H	A	W
I			W		A	W	A	S	H		D	
K	I	W	I		R		T		W	A	V	E
E			C		D	R	A	M	A		A	
N	O	V	E	L	S		R		R	U	N	G
E				I			R		T		C	
D	A	B	B	E	D		H	A	S	T	E	N
	W		E		E			C				E
S	K	I	M		C		P	E	T	E	R	S
	W		O	B	E	S	E		H			T
B	A	N	A		N		E		R	O	L	L
	R		N	I	C	E	R		O			E
O	D	E	S		Y		S	O	B	B	E	D

20

O	R	N	A	M	E	N	T		C	R	A	B
C			B		X		I		O			U
C	O	M	B		P	A	C	I	F	I	S	M
U			O		E		K		F			P
L	E	N	T	I	L		E		E			E
T		O		N		U	T	T	E	R	E	D
		R		T		S		U		I		
S	O	M	E	O	N	E		B		D		A
M			R		A		C	E	A	S	E	D
O			R		V		O		U			D
O	R	G	A	N	I	S	M		R	A	C	E
T			N		E		M		A			R
H	E	R	D		S	W	A	L	L	O	W	S

21

O	R	G	A	N		B		O		A		I
F			I		T	R	I	N	I	D	A	D
F	A	B	L	E		O		I		V		L
E			S	N	O	W	M	O	B	I	L	E
N		M		J				N		S		S
D	I	A	G	O	N	A	L		W	A	T	T
		S		Y		S		D		B		
D	E	S	K		A	S	S	A	I	L	E	D
R		A		S				N		E		O
I	N	C	O	H	E	R	E	N	T			N
N		R		A		E		Y	E	A	R	N
K	N	E	A	D	I	N	G		M			F
S		S		Y		T		S	P	E	N	D

22

U	N	N	A	M	E	D		O	V	A	R	Y
L			S			U		N		B		A
T		A	C	R	O	B	A	T		I		W
I			E			S		O	L	D	E	N
M	A	N	N	E	D		L			I		
A			T		I	M	A	G	I	N	E	D
T		P			G		U			G		E
E	X	A	C	T	I	N	G		C			P
		R			T		H	O	A	R	S	E
O	V	A	L	S		W			V			N
A		S		W	E	A	R	I	E	D		D
T		O		A		D			R			E
H	O	L	L	Y		S	P	O	N	G	E	D

23

E	N	R	A	G	E		P		W	E	P	T
N			G		S	I	E	V	E		A	
S	A	G	A		S		B		I	T	C	H
I			I		A	M	B	E	R		K	
G	R	A	N	N	Y		L		D	R	A	B
N				A			E		E		G	
S	A	V	A	G	E		S	C	R	E	E	N
	I		B		N			U				E
A	M	P	S		C		B	E	A	G	L	E
	L		C	R	A	W	L		I			D
C	E	D	E		S		A		D	U	L	L
	S		S	P	E	E	D		E			E
A	S	K	S		S		E	N	S	U	E	S

24

B	A	R	I	T	O	N	E		S	A	F	E
A			R		Z		M		E			D
N	I	C	K		O	R	B	I	T	I	N	G
I			E		N		R		T			I
S	U	B	D	U	E		Y		L			L
H		A		P		N	O	V	E	L	T	Y
		S		O		O		O		E		
G	R	E	E	N	E	R		T		W		A
A			M		L		D	E	A	D	E	N
F			B		I		O		D			O
F	I	N	A	N	C	E	D		M	I	L	D
E			R		I		G		I			E
D	U	N	K		T	H	E	A	T	R	E	S

SOLUTIONS

25

P	O	L	A	R		A		L		A		A
A			X		A	B	S	O	L	V	E	D
T	I	B	I	A		L		O		O		V
R			S	T	R	E	A	M	L	I	N	E
O		P		O				S		D		R
N	E	A	R	N	E	S	S		L	A	M	B
		R		E		E		C		N		
Q	U	A	Y		E	X	P	L	I	C	I	T
U		M		A				A		E		R
E	V	E	R	G	R	E	E	N	S			A
A		D		E		Y		S	A	V	E	D
S	K	I	N	N	I	E	R		N			E
Y		C		T		S		O	G	R	E	S

29

C	H	A	O	S		A		C		F		S
A			U		A	P	I	A	R	I	S	T
V	O	I	C	E		E		T		L		A
I			H	A	N	D	I	C	R	A	F	T
N		C		V				H		M		E
G	R	A	C	E	F	U	L		M	E	A	D
		V		S		R		V		N		
B	R	A	G		U	N	F	A	S	T	E	N
R		L		P				U		S		E
A	C	C	E	S	S	I	B	L	E			E
N		A		A		N		T	A	P	E	D
C	U	D	D	L	I	N	G		S			E
H		E		M		S		T	Y	P	E	D

26

T	E	D	I	O	U	S		O	T	H	E	R
R			N			E		P		E		I
I		S	U	L	T	A	N	A		R		C
B			R			M		L	E	A	S	H
U	N	B	E	N	D		S			L		
N			D		E	N	K	I	N	D	L	E
A		A			B		I			S		P
L	O	B	B	Y	I	S	T		P			I
		R			T		S	H	A	V	E	D
Q	U	A	C	K		E			U			E
U		D		N	O	B	L	E	S	T		M
I		E		E		B			E			I
T	A	S	T	E		S	E	I	S	M	I	C

30

C	O	P	P	E	R		O		H	A	W	K
A			A		U	N	C	L	E		E	
B	R	E	D		S		E		M	E	A	L
I			R		T	R	A	I	L		R	
N	A	M	E	L	Y		N		I	R	I	S
E				E			I		N		N	
T	A	R	M	A	C		C	L	E	R	G	Y
	V		A		O			E				I
S	E	E	M		N		C	I	R	C	L	E
	R		M	A	C	H	O		U			L
L	A	V	A		E		V		L	A	N	D
	G		L	E	A	V	E		E			E
B	E	D	S		L		N	U	R	S	E	D

27

O	N	W	A	R	D		O		D	I	A	L
R			L		E	M	B	E	R		C	
D	U	E	L		U		T		E	X	A	M
E			O		C	O	A	T	S		D	
R	U	S	T	L	E		I		S	E	E	S
L				I			N		E		M	
Y	A	C	H	T	S		S	P	R	A	Y	S
	N		Y		C			E				U
B	A	N	G		O		H	A	B	I	T	S
	T		I	G	L	O	O		A			T
G	O	N	E		D		M		L	A	M	A
	M		N	I	E	C	E		S			I
L	Y	R	E		D		S	H	A	K	E	N

31

G	R	E	A	T	E	S	T		O	V	E	N
A			M		X		R		T			I
P	L	E	A		I	N	A	C	T	I	O	N
I			S		T		N		E			E
N	O	I	S	E	S		C		R			T
G		R		L		S	E	N	S	O	R	Y
		O		M		A		O		V		
D	Y	N	A	S	T	Y		T		E		B
R			L		H		D	E	A	R	E	R
A			T		E		I		N			O
G	I	R	A	F	F	E	S		N	O	O	K
O			R		T		C		U			E
N	U	T	S		S	H	O	U	L	D	E	R

28

Q	U	E	A	S	I	E	R		L	I	M	P
U			T		S		E		I			A
E	V	I	L		S	H	A	M	B	L	E	D
S			A		U		D		E			D
T	U	S	S	L	E		E		L			E
S		O		U		F	R	I	S	K	E	D
		W		T		I		N		I		
S	U	S	P	E	C	T		K		L		A
O			H		L		C	Y	C	L	E	D
R			L		A		O		I			U
R	E	D	E	S	I	G	N		G	I	L	L
O			G		M		G		A			T
W	H	O	M		S	P	A	R	R	O	W	S

32

L	U	M	P	S		F		U		R		L
O			E		M	E	A	N	T	I	M	E
I	D	E	A	L		T		I		D		S
T			T	A	P	E	S	T	R	I	E	S
E		P		T				E		C		E
R	E	A	C	H	I	N	G		C	U	T	E
		R		E		I		F		L		
B	R	A	T		S	P	E	A	K	E	R	S
A		K		F				B		D		A
N	E	E	D	L	E	S	S	L	Y			N
G		E		O		A		E	A	S	E	D
L	E	T	H	A	R	G	Y		N			A
E		S		T		E		S	K	U	L	L

33

V	A	C	A	T	E	D		U	R	B	A	N
I			L			E		N		E		E
N		G	L	A	N	C	E	D		N		X
E			I			K		O	V	E	R	T
Y	O	D	E	L	S		M			F		
A			S		T	R	E	A	T	I	N	G
H		P			O		S			I		H
D	I	A	G	R	A	M	S		A			A
		N			T		Y	E	L	P	E	D
F	R	A	N	K		W			L			U
R		C		E	L	A	P	S	E	D		A
O		H		Y		I			G			T
G	U	E	S	S		L	O	Z	E	N	G	E

34

F	I	N	A	L	E		M		V	O	W	S
E			I		Q	U	E	U	E		R	
A	G	E	S		U		R		N	E	O	N
T			L		I	N	G	O	T		N	
U	P	K	E	E	P		I		U	R	G	E
R				V			N		R		E	
E	A	G	L	E	T		G	R	E	E	D	Y
	R		E		O			Y				E
A	C	H	E		W		W	E	A	S	E	L
	H		C	H	A	S	E		S			L
F	I	S	H		R		E		K	I	L	O
	N		E	N	D	E	D		E			W
E	G	G	S		S		S	E	W	E	R	S

35

H	A	N	D	I	E	S	T		H	E	R	B
I			O		M		H		E			R
G	N	U	S		B	E	A	R	A	B	L	E
H			E		E		T		V			W
L	O	A	D	E	D		C		E			E
Y		L		V		C	H	A	N	C	E	D
		S		E		O		Q		U		
D	R	O	W	N	E	D		U		R		W
E			I		V		R	A	M	B	L	E
B			Z		I		A		O			D
R	O	M	A	N	C	E	D		W	A	N	D
I			R		T		I		E			E
S	H	O	D		S	W	I	N	D	L	E	D

36

Y	O	K	E	S		A		I		O		G
O			K		I	N	E	D	I	B	L	E
U	P	S	E	T		T		I		N		I
T			S	E	M	I	C	O	L	O	N	S
H		B		A				M		X		H
S	C	A	R	C	E	L	Y		V	I	S	A
		D		H		O		R		O		
L	A	M	P		A	P	T	I	T	U	D	E
I		I		C				N		S		I
K	I	N	D	L	I	N	E	S	S			T
E		T		E		U		E	A	R	T	H
L	E	O	T	A	R	D	S		P			E
Y		N		N		E		A	S	T	I	R

37

O	P	T	I	C	A	L		A	W	A	R	E
B			C			U		L		R		W
L		D	E	F	I	C	I	T		C		E
I			C			K		O	T	H	E	R
G	R	E	A	S	E		O			A		
I			P		T	A	B	L	O	I	D	S
N		V			H		E			C		I
G	R	A	T	U	I	T	Y		M			M
		M			C		S	Q	U	I	R	M
I	M	P	E	L		M			T			E
C		I		U	N	E	Q	U	A	L		R
E		R		S		N			T			E
D	W	E	L	T		U	S	H	E	R	E	D

38

H	E	R	M	I	T		A		F	L	A	T
A			O		A	M	B	L	E		L	
T	A	L	C		I		S		S	O	B	S
C			K		L	I	C	I	T		I	
H	O	R	S	E	S		O		E	O	N	S
E				A			N		R		O	
D	A	U	N	T	S		D	E	S	I	S	T
	V		U		P			G				O
D	A	T	A		E		F	O	A	M	E	D
	R		N	I	C	H	E		T			D
Z	I	N	C		I		V		T	O	I	L
	C		E	V	A	D	E		I			E
H	E	M	S		L		R	I	C	H	E	R

39

P	I	T	T	A	N	C	E		H	A	N	G
O			H		O		N		O			L
N	A	P	E		T	O	R	T	O	I	S	E
C			I		C		I		V			A
H	E	A	R	T	H		C		E			N
O		X		O		P	H	Y	S	I	C	S
		L		T		I		O		C		
T	R	E	A	S	O	N		G		O		A
E			N		B		E	A	R	N	E	D
M			S		O		I		U			O
P	R	O	W	L	I	N	G		P	I	E	R
T			E		S		H		E			E
S	T	A	R		T	A	T	T	E	R	E	D

40

R	E	G	A	L		S		G		A		B
A			R		S	K	E	L	E	T	A	L
R	O	O	M	S		I		O		T		A
I			S	K	A	T	E	B	O	A	R	D
T		C		U				E		C		E
Y	E	A	R	N	I	N	G		S	K	I	S
		T		K		A		A		E		
F	L	A	N		O	B	S	C	U	R	E	D
A		R		S				O		S		E
C	H	A	R	A	C	T	E	R	S			F
A		C		L		U		N	A	I	V	E
D	E	T	R	A	C	T	S		N			N
E		S		D		U		E	D	G	E	D

41

D	E	L	A	Y	E	D		D	A	R	E	D
I			B			R		O		E		A
R		M	U	S	T	A	N	G		G		Z
E			S			G		S	N	A	R	E
C	I	N	E	M	A		P			L		
T			S		T	R	A	M	P	I	N	G
E		P			O		N			A		A
D	I	S	A	B	L	E	D		V			R
		Y			L		A	B	A	T	E	D
V	O	C	A	L		C			L			E
O		H		E	X	A	C	T	E	D		N
I		I		A		L			T			E
D	I	C	E	D		F	R	E	S	H	E	R

42

O	U	T	B	I	D		P		A	I	R	Y
R			I		I	R	A	T	E		E	
C	U	E	D		M		R		R	E	A	L
H			E		L	A	S	S	O		L	
A	V	I	D	L	Y		N		B	O	I	L
R				E			I		I		G	
D	A	I	N	T	Y		P	A	C	I	N	G
	N		E		O			Y				A
S	C	A	R		U		P	E	A	L	E	D
	H		V	I	N	Y	L		N			G
S	O	L	O		G		U		G	I	B	E
	V		U	S	E	R	S		L			T
E	Y	E	S		R		H	Y	E	N	A	S

43

W	A	S	T	E	F	U	L		P	L	O	P
A			A		A		I		E			U
K	I	N	K		S	C	A	B	B	A	R	D
I			E		T		B		B			D
N	O	O	S	E	S		L		L			L
G		U		A		R	E	C	E	I	V	E
		Z		R		I		O		D		
F	L	O	T	S	A	M		L		L		S
L			R		N		O	D	D	E	S	T
O			I		C		A		U			A
P	R	E	A	C	H	E	S		K	I	N	G
P			L		O		I		E			E
Y	A	M	S		R	E	S	I	S	T	E	D

44

P	E	T	A	L		T		R		C		A
A			C		C	O	V	E	T	O	U	S
Y	A	R	N	S		O		I		N		Y
E			E	C	O	L	O	G	I	C	A	L
E		M		A				N		O		U
S	H	A	B	B	I	E	R		S	C	U	M
		R		S		Y		H		T		
A	T	O	M		D	E	C	A	D	E	N	T
U		O		M				I		D		R
D	I	N	N	E	R	W	A	R	E			E
I		I		D		I		S	E	P	I	A
T	E	N	T	A	C	L	E		L			D
S		G		L		D		A	S	H	E	S

45

T	W	E	A	K	E	D		B	U	G	L	E
H			S			I		A		E		W
R		S	T	E	L	L	A	R		T		E
O			R			L		S	O	A	K	S
W	R	E	A	T	H		P			W		
I			L		A	N	A	G	R	A	M	S
N		M			T		I			Y		A
G	R	A	N	D	E	U	R		C			D
		S			S		S	T	A	Y	E	D
V	I	C	A	R		B			R			E
I		A		U	N	A	R	M	E	D		N
E		R		E		R			S			E
S	T	A	I	D		B	R	U	S	H	E	D

46

L	E	T	H	A	L		E		K	I	C	K
A			E		L	E	A	S	E		H	
R	E	N	D		A		R		N	E	A	R
G			G		M	E	L	O	N		T	
E	C	Z	E	M	A		I		E	V	E	R
S				A			E		L		A	
T	A	W	D	R	Y		R	E	S	C	U	E
	C		I		A			R				X
T	R	I	O		W		F	E	E	B	L	E
	E		C	A	N	O	E		L			M
R	A	G	E		I		W		B	L	I	P
	G		S	E	N	S	E		O			T
H	E	R	E		G		R	O	W	E	R	S

47

O	R	N	A	T	E	L	Y		G	O	L	F
X			D		V		E		U			U
Y	A	R	D		I	M	A	G	I	N	E	S
G			L		L		R		N			S
E	M	B	E	R	S		L		E			E
N		L		A		D	Y	N	A	M	O	S
		O		T		O		O		A		
S	U	B	J	E	C	T		S		I		B
P			A		O		K	E	E	N	E	R
O			B		W		U		V			E
O	U	T	B	O	A	R	D		O	G	R	E
K			E		R		O		K			Z
Y	O	U	R		D	I	S	P	E	N	S	E

48

H	U	M	A	N		G		M		F		S
O			W		P	H	E	A	S	A	N	T
I	N	S	E	T		E		S		N		A
S			S	A	U	E	R	K	R	A	U	T
T		W		B				S		T		U
S	T	A	B	B	I	N	G		B	I	T	E
		R		Y		I		K		C		
M	O	P	E		P	L	E	A	S	A	N	T
I		L		K				P		L		O
M	E	A	N	I	N	G	F	U	L			U
I		N		W		U		T	A	M	E	R
N	E	E	D	I	E	S	T		R			E
G		S		S		H		A	D	D	E	D

49

B	O	T	A	N	I	C		D	I	R	T	Y
A			R			H		A		E		O
C		T	E	N	S	I	O	N		M		L
K			N			T		K	N	A	C	K
D	I	L	A	T	E		P			T		
A			S		D	I	A	L	E	C	T	S
T		M			I		N			H		H
E	M	A	N	A	T	E	S		R			A
		R			S		Y	E	L	L	E	D
W	I	R	E	D		D			O			O
I		I		U	R	A	N	I	U	M		W
N		E		L		U			S			E
G	I	D	D	Y		B	R	I	E	F	E	D

50

G	L	O	A	T	S		I		G	O	A	T
A			L		H	U	N	C	H		M	
W	A	S	P		A		T		O	R	A	L
K			H		K	E	E	P	S		I	
I	N	V	A	D	E		R		T	H	E	Y
N				U			I		L		U	
G	A	R	A	G	E		M	A	Y	O	R	S
	C		D		M			I				U
A	C	I	D		B		O	D	I	O	U	S
	R		R	E	A	L	M		N			P
C	U	B	E		R		I		C	A	G	E
	E		S	I	G	H	T		U			N
A	S	P	S		O		S	T	R	A	N	D

51

W	H	E	A	T		S		J		S		S
A			K		S	M	O	O	T	H	L	Y
G	E	N	I	E		O		L		O		S
I			N	A	U	G	H	T	I	E	S	T
N		B		S				S		M		E
G	A	R	M	E	N	T	S		F	A	R	M
		O		L		U		D		K		
G	N	A	W		U	G	L	I	N	E	S	S
A		D		F				T		R		H
D	E	C	E	L	E	R	A	T	E			I
G		A		O		E		O	L	I	V	E
E	N	S	L	A	V	E	D		K			L
T		T		T		F		A	S	K	E	D

52

M	U	N	D	A	N	E		R	O	Y	A	L
E			O			D		O		A		E
G		G	U	A	R	D	E	D		P		E
A			B			Y		S	U	P	E	R
S	T	A	L	K	S		P			I		
T			E		P	L	A	T	O	N	I	C
A		S			I		I			G		U
R	E	A	P	P	E	A	R		S			R
		T			S		S	T	A	R	E	D
R	O	A	D	S		R			F			L
O		N		L	E	A	T	H	E	R		I
A		I		O		M			T			N
M	A	C	A	W		P	R	A	Y	I	N	G

53

M	O	S	A	I	C		T		T	H	A	T
E			V		H	E	A	V	E		C	
E	C	H	O		U		R		T	A	C	T
K			I		M	E	D	I	A		L	
E	L	U	D	E	S		I		N	E	A	T
S				L			E		U		I	
T	A	R	I	F	F		R	E	S	U	M	E
	B		N		O			L				A
C	Y	S	T		R		S	M	A	R	T	S
	S		O	R	B	I	T		M			T
O	M	E	N		I		O		E	P	E	E
	A		E	L	D	E	R		N			R
G	L	A	D		S		M	O	D	E	R	N

54

H	O	T	E	L	I	E	R		U	L	N	A
E			D		D		E		T			U
A	G	O	G		O	N	C	O	M	I	N	G
R			E		L		I		O			U
S	P	A	D	E	S		P		S			S
E		R		A		W	E	T	T	E	S	T
		E		S		A		U		P		
C	H	A	L	E	T	S		N		I		S
H			I		I		P	A	R	C	E	L
R			M		S		A		O			I
O	U	T	P	O	S	T	S		U	S	E	D
M			L		U		T		T			F
E	S	P	Y		E	L	E	M	E	N	T	S

55

O	C	E	A	N		L		B		H		P
Y			I		L	I	V	E	L	I	E	R
S	L	I	M	Y		E		F		G		I
T			S	A	N	D	W	I	C	H	E	S
E		A		N				T		L		O
R	E	B	U	K	I	N	G		K	I	L	N
		D		S		O		S		G		
D	R	U	G		T	W	I	T	C	H	E	D
E		C		S				R		T		R
M	E	T	I	C	U	L	O	U	S			E
O		I		R		A		T	A	X	E	D
T	A	N	K	A	R	D	S		V			G
E		G		P		Y		P	E	A	C	E

56

S	H	E	R	I	F	F		E	X	A	M	S
O			E			I		R		L		O
M		S	C	A	T	T	E	R		M		L
E			E			S		S	C	A	L	D
B	U	D	D	E	D		T			N		
O			E		E	V	A	L	U	A	T	E
D		S			N		N			C		P
Y	A	C	H	T	I	N	G		D			I
		H			M		Y	I	E	L	D	S
C	R	O	W	D		T			M			T
O		L		R	E	A	C	H	E	S		L
N		A		A		U			A			E
S	T	R	U	M		T	W	I	N	G	E	S

SOLUTIONS

57

B	E	W	A	R	E		I		S	W	A	B
A			U		N	I	G	H	T		R	
B	I	R	D		A		N		I	N	C	H
Y			I		C	L	I	F	F		A	
I	M	P	O	R	T		T		L	I	D	S
S				O			E		E		E	
H	A	N	D	E	D		D	I	S	U	S	E
	L		I		E			R				N
C	L	U	E		M		S	K	A	T	E	D
	E		T	I	A	R	A		L			U
T	R	E	E		N		L		B	E	A	R
	G		R	O	D	E	O		U			E
D	Y	E	S		S		N	U	M	B	E	D

58

C	H	O	R	U	S	E	D		I	O	T	A
H			E		O		A		N			R
I	S	L	E		R	E	M	O	T	E	S	T
L			K		E		A		E			I
L	E	N	S	E	S		G		N			S
S		U		L		V	E	R	D	I	C	T
		L		S		E		A		D		
H	O	L	I	E	S	T		V		E		T
E			N		A		N	E	G	A	T	E
R			N		U		O		U			N
B	A	L	A	N	C	E	D		I	C	E	S
A			T		E		E		S			E
L	O	D	E		R	E	S	P	E	C	T	S

59

A	L	I	B	I		A		P		F		U
N			E		A	V	I	A	T	I	O	N
K	E	B	A	B		O		T		R		I
L			D	R	O	W	S	I	N	E	S	S
E		C		E				O		P		E
S	E	A	F	A	R	E	R		C	O	A	X
		T		K		K		R		W		
O	M	A	R		S	E	D	A	T	E	L	Y
F		M		E				I		R		E
F	R	A	U	D	U	L	E	N	T			L
I		R		I		O		Y	O	D	E	L
C	H	A	R	C	O	A	L		W			O
E		N		T		N		E	N	D	O	W

60

Y	A	N	G	T	Z	E		E	M	P	T	Y
O			A			V		A		A		O
S		U	G	L	I	E	S	T		R		K
E			G			N		S	T	A	T	E
M	E	T	E	O	R		H			D		
I			D		O	R	A	T	I	O	N	S
T		L			L		R			X		H
E	V	A	C	U	E	E	S		C			O
		N			S		H	E	A	L	E	D
Q	U	O	T	E		J			M			D
U		L		R	E	A	C	T	E	D		I
I		I		A		M			R			E
Z	O	N	E	S		B	L	E	A	K	E	R

61

E	N	I	G	M	A		S		D	O	C	K
X			E		B	I	N	G	E		H	
H	E	I	R		O		A		L	O	A	F
A			M		V	A	G	U	E		R	
L	A	S	S	I	E		G		T	R	A	Y
E				L			E		E		D	
D	A	B	B	L	E		D	A	S	H	E	D
	N		E		N			R				O
I	N	K	S		H		S	C	A	R	E	D
	U		E	R	A	S	E		R			D
G	I	V	E		N		X		G	O	R	E
	T		C	Y	C	L	E		U			R
M	Y	T	H		E		S	T	E	A	M	Y

62

E	L	I	T	E		M		D		N		E
V			E		V	E	T	E	R	A	N	S
O	F	F	A	L		T		C		R		T
L			R	A	C	E	C	O	U	R	S	E
V		P		D				R		O		E
E	N	A	B	L	I	N	G		S	W	U	M
		R		E		O		E		I		
J	O	B	S		O	D	D	M	E	N	T	S
A		O		B				I		G		O
G	U	I	T	A	R	I	S	T	S			N
G		L		I		B		S	A	U	N	A
E	L	E	C	T	R	I	C		L			T
D		D		S		S		D	E	L	T	A

63

F	A	C	T	U	A	L		G	L	A	N	D
O			I			E		L		F		I
R		S	T	O	R	A	G	E		F		R
E			L			N		E	X	A	C	T
M	Y	S	E	L	F		M			I		
O			D		U	N	A	W	A	R	E	S
S		C			S		R			S		T
T	R	A	I	N	E	E	S		B			A
		N			D		H	E	R	O	I	N
M	E	A	L	S		G			E			D
A		S		W	E	A	T	H	E	R		A
I		T		A		L			Z			R
M	E	A	N	T		A	D	H	E	R	E	D

64

A	R	T	F	U	L		I		N	I	B	S
T			L		I	N	T	R	O		I	
H	E	R	O		M		A		O	N	C	E
E			R		I	D	L	E	D		Y	
I	M	P	A	C	T		I		L	I	C	E
S				O			C		E		L	
M	A	N	A	G	E		S	A	S	H	E	S
	M		D		J			L				T
P	A	L	M		E		D	E	E	P	E	R
	Z		I	T	C	H	Y		A			I
T	I	E	R		T		K		G	O	A	D
	N		E	L	O	P	E		L			E
A	G	E	D		R		S	P	E	E	D	S

65

N	I	M	B	L	E	S	T		R	I	N	D
U			L		N		H		O			E
R	U	D	E		S	T	R	O	L	L	E	D
S			E		U		O		L			U
E	L	A	P	S	E		A		E			C
S		R		A		S	T	A	R	L	E	T
		I		R		I		L		O		
G	L	A	C	I	E	R		T		T		P
U			H		M		T	O	A	S	T	S
T			E		E		A		B			A
T	E	L	E	G	R	A	M		H	A	I	L
E			S		G		E		O			M
R	O	D	E		E	A	R	D	R	U	M	S

69

R	E	P	R	I	S	A	L		W	O	R	D
E			E		O		I		A			O
W	E	L	D		B	A	K	E	R	I	E	S
A			I		E		E		B			A
R	U	D	D	E	R		N		L			G
D		U		A		E	S	S	E	N	C	E
		N		R		W		A		A		
C	L	E	A	N	S	E		M		I		E
A			B		E		B	E	D	L	A	M
D			R		E		A		A			D
G	L	O	A	T	I	N	G		R	A	R	E
E			D		N		E		N			D
D	I	N	E		G	A	L	O	S	H	E	S

66

N	O	M	A	D		K		A		P		R
I			F		D	I	S	G	R	A	C	E
C	L	O	A	K		W		O		D		T
H			R	A	T	I	O	N	A	L	L	Y
E		J		R				Y		O		P
S	H	A	M	M	I	N	G		A	C	R	E
		Y		A		A		S		K		
L	A	W	N		E	Y	E	T	E	E	T	H
U		A		S				U		D		A
R	E	L	U	C	T	A	N	C	E			C
I		K		A		U		K	A	Y	A	K
N	E	E	D	L	I	N	G		C			E
G		R		Y		T		C	H	O	R	D

70

P	R	O	V	E		S		C		S		F
U			E		S	E	A	R	C	H	E	R
F	A	T	A	L		A		I		R		I
F			L	A	U	N	D	E	R	I	N	G
E		A		I				D		E		I
D	E	B	A	R	R	E	D		S	K	I	D
		R		S		B		P		I		
Y	E	A	R		O	B	T	A	I	N	E	D
E		S		S				G		G		A
A	R	I	S	T	O	C	R	A	T			W
R		V		A		A		N	A	M	E	D
N	E	E	D	L	E	S	S		C			L
S		S		L		E		W	O	R	S	E

67

L	O	C	A	T	E	D		E	A	R	L	Y
I			N			R		Y		E		E
T		A	G	I	T	A	T	E		G		L
I			E			W		D	R	A	W	L
G	L	A	R	E	D		B			L		
A			S		Y	O	U	N	G	E	S	T
N		U			I		R			D		H
T	A	N	G	E	N	T	S		D			W
		E			G		T	R	A	U	M	A
T	E	A	S	E		B			N			R
W		I		D	I	A	G	R	A	M		T
I		E		G		T			N			F
G	E	N	R	E		S	W	E	A	T	E	D

71

D	Y	N	A	M	I	C		C	U	F	F	S
O			V			A		A		O		A
W		F	E	L	I	N	E	S		R		N
N			R			E		H	O	A	R	D
H	O	U	S	E	D		A			G		
I			E		I	N	C	I	D	E	N	T
L		A			V		H			S		E
L	I	B	E	R	A	T	E		L			T
		I			S		S	T	A	R	C	H
A	I	D	E	D		L			T			E
U		I		O	R	A	N	G	E	S		R
R		N		L		R			N			E
A	N	G	E	L		K	N	O	T	T	E	D

68

S	I	L	V	E	R		F		B	O	A	T
I			I		I	M	A	G	E		R	
Z	E	A	L		N		N		L	I	M	E
Z			L		G	U	A	V	A		R	
L	I	L	A	C	S		T		T	I	E	D
E				A			I		E		S	
D	A	Z	I	N	G		C	A	D	E	T	S
	V		M		A			P				A
W	O	M	B		T		S	E	A	L	E	D
	C		I	N	E	P	T		F			D
G	A	R	B		W		E		F	O	I	L
	D		E	L	A	T	E		I			E
L	O	R	D		Y		P	I	X	I	E	S

72

U	N	P	A	I	D		M		L	E	A	F
N			M		E	N	E	M	Y		M	
C	R	A	B		N		A		N	A	B	S
L			E		T	U	N	I	C		L	
E	X	T	R	A	S		D		H	A	I	R
A				I			E		E		N	
R	A	B	B	L	E		R	E	S	I	G	N
	N		L		Y			E				U
H	Y	P	E		E		B	L	A	M	E	D
	T		N	O	B	L	E		N			I
F	I	N	D		R		S		V	A	N	S
	M		E	R	O	D	E		I			T
D	E	E	D		W		T	A	L	O	N	S

SOLUTIONS

73

V	O	L	A	T	I	L	E		I	D	O	L
A			L		N		N		N			O
I	N	T	O		T	H	A	T	C	H	E	D
N			U		E		M		O			G
L	E	A	D	E	R		E		M			E
Y		M		D		F	L	E	E	C	E	S
		I		I		A		V		O		
U	P	D	A	T	E	D		I		R		A
N			T		N		C	L	O	N	E	D
E			T		V		I		G			D
V	A	C	A	T	I	N	G		R	U	L	E
E			C		E		A		E			R
N	I	C	K		S	T	R	E	S	S	E	S

74

K	N	E	A	D		O		A		I		A
I			L		A	B	S	C	O	N	D	S
D	R	E	A	M		O		U		D		T
N			S	E	V	E	N	T	I	E	T	H
A		M		T				E		C		M
P	L	A	C	A	R	D	S		T	O	G	A
		R		L		U		M		R		
G	U	M	S		M	O	L	E	C	U	L	E
O		A		J				N		M		V
V	I	L	L	A	I	N	O	U	S			A
E		A		P		E		S	I	T	E	D
R	A	D	I	A	N	C	E		C			E
N		E		N		K		S	K	I	E	D

75

Y	A	N	K	I	N	G		R	E	A	C	H
O			O			R		O		S		O
U		P	A	P	R	I	K	A		S		N
T			L			T		D	E	U	C	E
H	A	Z	A	R	D		P			M		
F			S		E	V	A	C	U	E	E	S
U		P			N		N			S		P
L	E	A	R	N	I	N	G		K			E
		R			M		S	T	A	T	I	C
R	O	A	M	S		S			R			T
U		S		L	O	C	K	J	A	W		R
M		O		E		A			T			U
P	I	L	E	D		B	O	R	E	D	O	M

76

R	I	B	A	L	D		J		M	O	A	T
E			W		I	N	A	N	E		G	
H	U	L	A		E		B		M	O	A	N
O			K		T	A	B	L	E		I	
U	D	D	E	R	S		I		N	O	N	E
S				U			N		T		S	
E	A	S	I	E	R		G	H	O	S	T	S
	N		N		E			O				C
S	T	U	D		L		H	E	A	L	T	H
	H		O	V	A	R	Y		S			E
V	E	T	O		P		E		H	A	R	M
	M		R	I	S	E	N		E			E
U	S	E	S		E		A	N	N	A	L	S

77

L	I	G	A	M	E	N	T		Y	A	W	N
O			W		L		E		A			I
T	U	B	A		F	L	A	G	P	O	L	E
I			S		I		P		P			C
O	R	P	H	A	N		O		E			E
N		E		J		S	T	U	D	I	E	S
		E		A		U		P		O		
A	S	P	I	R	I	N		O		N		U
B			S		N		U	N	I	S	O	N
A			S		C		N		G			I
C	R	O	U	C	H	E	D		L	E	F	T
U			E		E		U		O			E
S	E	N	D		S	T	E	R	O	I	D	S

78

S	W	I	F	T		C		A		O		B
I			E		P	R	O	B	A	B	L	E
T	R	E	A	D		I		O		L		H
T			T	A	M	B	O	U	R	I	N	E
E		B		I				T		V		A
R	E	A	S	S	U	R	E		P	I	E	D
		R		Y		I		S		O		
C	U	B	S		A	P	P	L	A	U	S	E
O		E		L				U		S		M
B	U	C	C	A	N	E	E	R	S			B
R		U		N		A		P	A	S	T	A
A	N	E	C	D	O	T	E		W			R
S		D		S		S		K	N	O	C	K

79

H	U	S	B	A	N	D		R	E	F	E	R
A			E			E		A		L		O
T		C	H	I	E	F	L	Y		O		P
C			A			Y		S	P	A	C	E
H	U	R	L	E	D		A			T		
I			F		I	N	D	E	C	E	N	T
N		D			G		A			D		R
G	R	A	B	B	I	N	G		C			U
		Z			T		E	N	A	C	T	S
G	A	Z	E	S		F			R			T
I		L		W	E	A	R	I	E	S		F
S		E		A		M			E			U
T	E	D	D	Y		E	T	E	R	N	A	L

80

S	A	V	A	G	E		M		G	R	E	W
O			S		R	E	A	D	Y		M	
F	L	I	P		U		T		R	E	A	M
T			I		P	L	A	Z	A		N	
E	L	I	C	I	T		D		T	E	A	T
S				C			O		E		T	
T	A	N	D	E	M		R	E	D	D	E	N
	N		A		O			R				O
O	X	E	N		N		M	A	C	A	W	S
	I		C	R	A	Z	Y		I			I
M	O	L	E		R		R		G	O	N	E
	U		R	E	C	U	R		A			S
A	S	K	S		H		H	O	R	N	E	T

81

P	R	E	A	M	B	L	E		Z	A	N	Y
O			L		A		R		O			O
U	N	D	O		R	E	A	S	O	N	E	D
N			O		O		S		M			E
D	E	A	F	E	N		E		E			L
S		R		V		C	R	A	D	L	E	S
		E		I		A		N		O		
T	R	A	W	L	E	R		E		O		A
R			A		L		S	W	A	M	P	S
A			R		E		I		G			T
G	R	I	M	A	C	E	D		R	O	A	R
I			E		T		E		E			A
C	H	A	R		S	U	D	D	E	N	L	Y

82

M	U	M	B	L	E	D		C	A	L	L	S
O			R			O		E		O		L
T		D	I	A	M	O	N	D		Y		O
I			D			M		E	X	A	L	T
V	O	C	A	L	S		A			L		
A			L		L	A	M	E	N	T	E	D
T		H			Y		U			Y		O
E	X	A	M	P	L	E	S		C			M
		U			Y		E	N	A	B	L	E
A	T	L	A	S		H				V		S
N		A		T	R	A	W	L	E	R		T
N		G		A		L				R		I
E	N	E	M	Y		F	R	A	N	T	I	C

83

M	I	R	A	G	E		A		S	T	A	B
E			R		J	U	D	G	E		U	
T	A	K	E		E		V		C	O	C	K
H			N		C	H	A	I	R		T	
A	G	H	A	S	T		N		E	M	I	T
N			A				C		T		O	
E	D	I	C	T	S		E	A	S	I	N	G
	A		U		T		N					A
D	Y	E	D		R		I	D	I	O	M	S
	C		G	U	A	R	D		N			K
B	A	S	E		N		L		F	A	R	E
	R		L	E	D	G	E		E			T
H	E	R	S		S		S	I	R	E	N	S

84

C	O	N	C	O	C	T	S		L	A	M	A
A			R		O		Q		I			N
L	A	V	A		V	A	U	L	T	I	N	G
I			W		E		I		T			L
C	H	A	L	E	T		R		E			E
O		D		V		S	T	A	R	R	E	D
		E		I		A		B		O		
D	A	N	G	L	E	D		L		S		S
E			R		E		R	E	J	E	C	T
N			E		R		A		I			O
T	R	E	A	T	I	N	G		V	E	I	L
A			S		E		E		E			E
L	A	C	E		R	E	D	E	S	I	G	N

85

F	L	E	A	S		T		M		S		A
A			L		P	Y	R	A	M	I	D	S
T	R	I	P	E		P		I		M		C
H			S	T	R	E	A	M	L	I	N	E
E		P		H				S		L		N
R	E	A	L	I	S	T	S		V	A	S	T
		R		C		O		A		R		
P	L	A	Y		T	W	I	D	D	L	E	D
I		G		A				O		Y		E
C	A	R	I	C	A	T	U	R	E			A
N		A		I		A		E	M	E	N	D
I	M	P	U	D	E	N	T		U			L
C		H		S		K		E	S	S	A	Y

86

E	R	R	A	T	I	C		T	A	P	E	R
M			I			A		E		O		E
P		S	T	R	A	T	U	M		N		I
O			A			S		P	E	C	A	N
W	O	O	I	N	G		R			H		
E			N		A	B	A	T	T	O	I	R
R		G			L		C			S		O
S	T	A	G	N	A	T	E		D			W
		R			S		D	R	A	P	E	D
E	D	G	E	S		F			H			I
W		L		I	R	A	T	E	L	Y		E
E		E		Z		C			I			S
R	I	D	G	E		E	X	H	A	U	S	T

87

I	G	U	A	N	A		P		S	O	C	K
L			U		P	L	A	C	E		H	
L	O	U	D		R		R		A	J	A	R
I			I		O	P	A	L	S		R	
C	A	R	T	O	N		D		O	H	M	S
I				W			E		N		E	
T	A	L	E	N	T		D	E	S	I	R	E
	B		N		R		G					A
H	O	G	S		A		D	O	C	T	O	R
	L		N	E	V	E	R		O			T
V	I	S	A		E		E		D	I	S	H
	S		R	I	L	E	S		E			E
S	H	O	E		S		S	O	D	D	E	N

88

T	E	N	D	E	R	E	D		J	O	K	E
H			U		O		I		A			N
A	G	E	S		M	I	R	A	C	L	E	S
N			T		P		E		K			U
K	I	O	S	K	S		C		A			E
S		W		E		S	T	A	L	K	E	D
		E		E		O		Q		N		
M	U	D	D	L	E	D		U		O		A
O			I		A		D	A	B	B	E	D
S			S		S		O		I			H
Q	U	I	C	K	E	S	T		G	A	P	E
U			O		L		E		O			R
E	G	G	S		S	E	D	A	T	I	V	E

SOLUTIONS

89

A	C	T	E	D		I		D		A		R
D			B		S	C	R	A	M	B	L	E
M	A	Y	B	E		O		T		R		G
I			S	A	U	N	T	E	R	I	N	G
R		I		R				S		D		A
E	N	D	A	N	G	E	R		O	G	L	E
		E		S		R		H		I		
Q	U	A	Y		O	R	D	A	I	N	E	D
U		L		H				V		G		O
O	R	I	G	I	N	A	T	E	D			O
T		S		V		X		N	A	K	E	D
E	X	T	R	E	M	E	S		M			L
S		S		S		D		S	P	I	T	E

90

L	O	C	A	L	L	Y		Q	U	A	K	E
O			N			A		U		W		K
U		D	I	L	E	M	M	A		K		E
N			M			S		D	O	W	N	S
G	R	O	A	N	S		S			A		
I			L		I	M	P	L	O	R	E	D
N		M			L		A			D		I
G	R	A	N	U	L	E	S		P			S
		L			Y		M	E	A	N	E	R
Q	U	A	C	K		P			U			O
U		R		I	M	A	G	I	N	E		B
I		I		T		S			C			E
P	H	A	S	E		O	R	C	H	A	R	D

91

P	U	R	R	E	D		R		L	E	A	P
I			A		E	L	E	G	Y		N	
L	I	M	B		C		C		N	I	C	E
L			B		R	E	L	I	C		H	
O	D	D	I	T	Y		A		H	O	O	T
W				A			I		E		R	
S	A	V	A	G	E		M	O	D	E	S	T
	I		D		X			R				O
P	R	O	D		P		O	B	E	Y	E	D
	L		L	E	A	R	N		X			D
M	I	N	I		N		S		P	I	L	L
	F		N	U	D	G	E		E			E
S	T	A	G		S		T	I	L	L	E	R

92

R	E	L	E	V	A	N	T		D	I	E	D
A			A		H		H		R			E
F	A	N	G		E	X	A	M	I	N	E	R
F			E		A		T		F			I
L	E	E	R	E	D		C		T			D
E		V		A		W	H	I	S	T	L	E
		E		R		A		T		I		
D	Y	N	A	S	T	Y		C		F		A
I			P		O		T	H	E	F	T	S
S			I		T		H		N			S
M	O	N	E	T	A	R	Y		D	A	Z	E
A			C		L		M		E			S
L	U	R	E		S	T	E	A	D	I	E	S

93

Q	U	E	R	Y		D		A		P		S
U			I		O	U	T	B	U	R	S	T
A	L	T	O	S		M		O		O		R
R			T	E	M	P	E	R	A	N	C	E
T		S		E				T		O		A
S	C	A	N	D	A	L	S		S	U	L	K
		L		Y		A		F		N		
Q	U	I	T		E	X	P	L	I	C	I	T
U		V		A				I		E		W
E	X	A	G	G	E	R	A	T	E			E
U		T		A		E		S	E	P	I	A
E	Y	E	L	I	N	E	R		L			K
S		S		N		L		I	S	L	E	S

94

A	B	R	A	D	E	D		T	W	A	N	G
D			I			U		U		L		E
M		A	R	C	H	A	I	C		I		N
I			M			L		K	N	A	V	E
T	H	R	A	S	H		O			S		
T			N		E	S	C	A	P	E	E	S
E		V			D		T			S		Y
D	I	A	L	O	G	U	E		M			N
		C			E		T	E	A	M	E	D
T	E	A	C	H		L			N			R
U		T		O	K	A	Y	I	N	G		O
F		E		L		M			E			M
T	O	D	A	Y		E	N	G	R	A	V	E

95

A	R	M	A	D	A		I		S	U	C	K
B			M		M	U	S	T	Y		R	
D	R	A	B		A		O		N	E	A	R
O			L		S	A	L	V	O		T	
M	E	L	E	E	S		A		N	E	E	D
E				R			T		Y		R	
N	A	B	B	E	D		E	N	M	E	S	H
	N		R		E			E				A
C	O	M	A		B		R	E	A	D	E	R
	T		G	R	A	C	E		D			N
T	H	U	G		T		N		D	O	Z	E
	E		E	V	E	N	T		E			S
G	R	I	D		S		S	I	D	L	E	S

96

R	U	N	A	W	A	Y	S		E	V	E	R
O			N		D		H		R			A
T	W	I	G		U	N	A	F	R	A	I	D
A			E		L		V		A			I
T	H	I	R	S	T		E		N			O
E		L		U		T	R	U	D	G	E	S
		L		R		H		R		U		
O	B	S	C	E	N	E		G		S		E
X			A		Y		N	E	A	T	E	R
Y			M		L		O		L			O
G	R	I	E	V	O	U	S		L	E	N	D
E			L		N		E		O			E
N	A	P	S		S	I	D	E	W	A	Y	S

97

E	Q	U	A	L		C		B		M		S
N			I		P	H	E	A	S	A	N	T
S	C	O	L	D		I		S		N		U
I			S	A	N	C	T	I	F	I	E	D
G		O		L				L		F		I
N	I	B	B	L	I	N	G		M	E	M	O
		T		Y		I		P		S		
C	L	A	N		O	B	J	E	C	T	E	D
A		I		L				N		O		A
R	A	N	S	A	C	K	I	N	G			R
O		I		Z		N		Y	E	A	R	N
L	I	N	G	E	R	E	D		A			E
S		G		D		E		F	R	A	U	D

98

T	A	I	L	I	N	G		A	W	A	R	D
O			A			O		I		R		U
B		O	R	C	H	A	R	D		R		L
O			I			L		S	H	A	L	L
G	L	E	A	M	S		P			Y		
G			T		M	E	A	N	D	E	R	S
A		S			E		D			D		H
N	E	C	K	B	A	N	D		P			A
		R			R		Y	E	L	P	E	D
A	L	A	R	M		F			F			I
N		P		A	N	A	G	R	A	M		E
T		E		Z		L			S			S
I	S	S	U	E		L	E	V	E	R	E	T

99

L	O	C	A	T	E		I		J	A	B	S
O			D		M	A	C	H	O		L	
Z	O	N	E		B		I		L	E	A	K
E			P		E	X	C	E	L		Z	
N	E	C	T	A	R		L		I	T	E	M
G				I			E		E		R	
E	A	T	E	R	S		S	O	R	E	S	T
	D		X		C			N				I
P	U	M	A		R		R	E	A	R	E	D
	L		C	E	A	S	E		I			I
P	A	S	T		T		N		S	W	A	N
	T		L	U	C	I	D		L			G
D	E	N	Y		H		S	H	E	A	R	S

100

U	N	R	A	V	E	L	S		V	E	R	B
N			D		N		P		I			U
W	I	L	D		J	E	A	L	O	U	S	Y
R			E		O		R		L			E
A	F	F	R	A	Y		S		A			R
P		O		L		C	E	N	S	O	R	S
		W		S		O		O		M		
B	A	L	L	O	O	N		T		I		C
U			L		F		G	E	N	T	L	Y
F			A		F		A		E			C
F	I	R	M	N	E	S	S		W	A	I	L
E			A		N		P		E			E
D	I	M	S		D	E	S	T	R	O	Y	S

101

U	R	B	A	N		G		G		O		U
S			W		G	R	A	N	D	S	O	N
U	S	U	A	L		I		A		T		U
R			Y	O	U	N	G	S	T	E	R	S
P		P		B				H		O		E
S	H	A	M	B	L	E	S		S	P	E	D
		T		Y		L		F		A		
J	A	R	S		S	K	E	L	E	T	A	L
U		I		R				O		H		E
M	E	A	N	I	N	G	F	U	L			W
B		R		G		A		T	A	M	E	D
L	U	C	K	I	E	S	T		I			L
E		H		D		H		I	R	O	N	Y

102

V	I	T	A	M	I	N		P	E	A	C	E
A			L			I		A		V		A
N		T	W	I	T	C	H	Y		I		R
I			A			K		S	H	A	W	L
S	T	A	Y	E	D		C			T		
H			S		A	B	A	N	D	O	N	S
E		B			N		U			R		H
D	I	A	L	E	C	T	S		S			A
		R			E		E	L	A	T	E	D
W	H	O	L	E		C			L			O
H		N		C	O	A	S	T	A	L		W
O		E		H		L			M			E
M	O	T	T	O		M	E	R	I	T	E	D

103

F	L	I	N	C	H		D		F	A	I	R
I			U		A	W	A	R	E		N	
F	L	E	D		R		M		R	E	D	O
T			E		P	L	A	I	T		U	
E	R	A	S	E	S		G		I	D	L	Y
E				L			E		L		G	
N	O	T	I	F	Y		D	I	E	T	E	D
	N		N		A			V				A
U	S	E	R		W		T	Y	P	I	F	Y
	H		O	U	N	C	E		I			T
S	O	Y	A		I		N		T	A	X	I
	R		D	I	N	E	D		C			M
N	E	T	S		G		S	P	H	E	R	E

104

T	H	O	U	S	A	N	D		B	A	R	B
U			N		C		E		E			A
G	N	A	W		R	E	A	W	A	K	E	N
G			E		E		L		C			T
E	V	A	D	E	S		E		O			E
D		R		X		D	R	I	N	K	E	R
		E		I		U		N		I		
G	R	A	F	T	E	D		K		L		A
L			E		F		H	Y	E	N	A	S
A			A		F		A		I			I
D	O	O	R	B	E	L	L		G	O	L	D
L			E		C		V		H			E
Y	A	R	D		T	R	E	A	T	I	E	S

105

S	N	I	F	F		S		R		E		A
E			A		E	M	B	O	S	S	E	D
C	I	R	C	A		U		V		T		A
T			T	O	U	G	H	E	N	I	N	G
O		C		R				D		M		E
R	E	A	C	T	I	O	N		D	A	I	S
		M		A		P		W		T		
R	E	E	F		S	T	R	A	T	E	G	Y
E		R		W				D		D		O
G	U	A	R	A	N	T	E	E	D			U
A		M		F		O		D	A	U	N	T
I	N	A	C	T	I	O	N		R			H
N		N		S		L		S	K	I	D	S

106

A	U	T	H	O	R	S		S	T	A	I	D
C			A			L		A		S		O
T		I	N	D	I	A	N	S		H		V
I			G			P		H	E	A	V	E
V	I	C	A	R	S		P			M		
A			R		H	E	A	D	S	E	T	S
T		C			O		N			D		A
E	M	A	N	A	T	E	D		T			D
		R			S		A	M	A	Z	E	D
F	I	N	D	S		D			V			E
L		A		W	R	A	P	P	E	R		N
E		G		A		T			R			E
W	H	E	L	P		A	V	E	N	G	E	D

107

P	A	L	A	T	E		M		L	A	Y	S
O			L		W	H	A	L	E		E	
R	A	S	P		E		N		N	U	L	L
T			H		R	O	A	S	T		L	
R	I	V	A	L	S		G		I	R	I	S
A				I			E		L		N	
Y	A	C	H	T	S		D	E	S	I	G	N
	I		A		A			M				O
T	R	O	T		T		N	U	G	G	E	T
	S		E	X	I	L	E		A			A
C	H	E	F		S		S		F	L	A	B
	I		U	N	F	I	T		F			L
O	P	A	L		Y		S	E	E	T	H	E

108

F	I	N	A	N	C	E	D		W	E	I	R
I			L		O		R		O			U
D	A	U	B		M	E	A	T	B	A	L	L
D			U		E		W		B			I
L	I	T	M	U	S		E		L			N
E		O		L		B	R	A	Y	I	N	G
		M		N		U		V		D		
S	U	B	W	A	Y	S		O		E		I
U			O		I		S	W	E	A	T	S
R			E		E		L		N			O
F	I	T	F	U	L	L	Y		D	U	M	B
E			U		D		E		O			A
D	I	L	L		S	H	R	E	W	D	E	R

109

K	E	B	A	B		D		S		P		G
N			C		M	O	R	T	G	A	G	E
O	U	G	H	T		L		U		N		I
C			E	A	V	E	S	D	R	O	P	S
K		S		B				S		R		H
S	H	A	B	B	I	E	R		J	A	V	A
		N		Y		L		D		M		
J	A	D	E		I	M	P	A	L	I	N	G
A		P		G				M		C		R
U	N	A	B	R	I	D	G	E	D			O
N		P		U		E		S	O	N	I	C
T	R	E	M	B	L	E	S		F			E
Y		R		S		R		O	F	F	E	R

110

O	V	A	T	I	O	N		F	U	N	G	I
B			I			I		I		E		N
I		B	A	T	H	T	U	B		G		C
T			R			S		S	T	A	S	H
U	N	S	A	I	D		L			T		
A			S		R	E	A	P	P	E	A	R
R		A			A		D			D		O
Y	U	L	E	T	I	D	E		W			S
		E			N		N	U	A	N	C	E
C	A	R	G	O		S			L			M
O		T		I	N	A	N	E	L	Y		A
M		E		L		N			E			R
B	I	D	E	S		G	R	A	T	I	F	Y

111

C	H	A	F	E	S		O		P	A	R	K
Y			R		C	O	D	E	S		E	
G	A	L	E		O		D		Y	O	G	A
N			E		P	A	N	I	C		A	
E	N	T	R	E	E		E		H	I	L	T
T				K			S		I		I	
S	A	U	C	E	R		S	O	C	I	A	L
	T		O		E			U				A
W	H	E	N		M		T	R	A	D	E	D
	E		T	R	A	C	E		S			D
K	I	L	O		T		P		H	I	R	E
	S		U	N	C	L	E		E			R
S	T	A	R		H		E	N	S	U	E	S

112

V	O	C	A	T	I	O	N		I	O	T	A
O			V		T		A		T			S
O	O	Z	E		E	P	I	T	A	P	H	S
D			R		M		L		L			U
O	R	A	T	E	S		E		I			R
O		C		W		E	D	U	C	A	T	E
		N		E		A		N		U		
D	R	E	S	S	E	R		I		T		S
E			A		X		U	T	M	O	S	T
N			L		E		N		O			I
I	N	C	U	R	R	E	D		R	U	F	F
A			T		T		I		A			L
L	O	N	E		S	I	D	E	L	I	N	E

113

U	P	P	E	R		E		M		R		A
N			O		S	P	E	A	K	E	R	S
F	A	U	N	A		I		I		S		T
O			S	P	E	C	U	L	A	T	O	R
L		W		P				S		R		A
D	E	A	D	L	O	C	K		K	I	L	L
		V		E		O		F		C		
A	X	E	S		R	O	M	A	N	T	I	C
R		B		R				I		S		H
C	H	A	R	A	C	T	E	R	S			A
H		N		D		O		Y	A	N	K	S
E	N	D	E	A	R	E	D		N			T
R		S		R		S		S	K	A	T	E

114

Q	U	I	B	B	L	E		C	U	B	E	S
U			R			D		U		O		P
I		R	E	S	I	D	U	E		T		E
V			A			Y		S	T	A	N	D
E	X	I	S	T	S		R			N		
R			T		A	P	I	A	R	I	E	S
E		C			R		N			C		H
D	I	A	G	R	A	M	S		B			R
		N			H		E	L	A	P	S	E
L	E	A	F	Y		I			G			D
O		S		O	R	B	I	T	E	D		D
O		T		L		I			L			E
K	N	A	C	K		S	M	A	S	H	E	D

115

K	H	Y	B	E	R		I		B	E	A	K
E			L		E	L	D	E	R		D	
E	P	E	E		N		Y		A	R	M	S
P			N		T	A	L	O	N		I	
E	X	U	D	E	S		L		D	A	R	E
R				N			I		E		A	
S	A	L	A	D	S		C	U	D	D	L	E
	V		I		O			R				N
H	E	R	B		C		I	N	B	R	E	D
	R		I	R	K	E	D		A			U
P	A	W	N		E		I		B	O	A	R
	G		O	U	T	D	O		E			E
L	E	I	S		S		T	O	S	S	E	D

116

S	E	P	A	R	A	T	E		R	O	A	M
I			B		R		X		E			A
S	O	D	A		C	L	A	M	B	E	R	S
T			T		E		L		A			O
E	X	C	E	E	D		T		T			N
R		L		A		A	S	C	E	N	D	S
		U		S		S		A		I		
R	O	B	B	E	R	S		W		N		S
E			E		A		A	S	L	E	E	P
A			H		B		G		O			A
S	Q	U	A	B	B	L	E		C	L	A	D
O			V		I		N		A			E
N	A	M	E		S	E	T	T	L	E	R	S

117

E	D	G	E	D		R		A		S		U
M			Y		W	I	N	G	S	P	A	N
B	R	E	E	D		L		I		O		I
A			S	A	T	E	L	L	I	T	E	S
L		C		U				E		L		E
M	E	A	N	N	E	S	S		J	I	N	X
		T		T		H		A		G		
M	E	A	D		L	E	N	G	T	H	E	N
E		R		F				O		T		E
T	R	A	D	I	T	I	O	N	S			C
E		C		E		M		Y	E	A	S	T
O	U	T	C	R	O	P	S		E			A
R		S		Y		S		A	S	T	I	R

118

A	C	T	R	E	S	S		L	I	V	E	R
L			O			O		O		I		E
L		S	W	A	B	B	E	D		T		F
O			I			S		E	X	A	M	S
W	A	R	N	E	D		A			M		
I			G		I	M	B	I	B	I	N	G
N		G			V		Y			N		U
G	L	A	C	I	E	R	S		R			I
		G			D		S	C	A	R	E	D
M	O	G	U	L		W			N			A
A		I		A	V	A	R	I	C	E		N
I		N		G		R			I			C
T	O	G	A	S		T	W	I	D	D	L	E

119

K	A	Y	A	K	S		R		W	E	B	S
I			D		W	E	A	V	E		U	
S	E	E	D		I		V		L	A	D	Y
S			L		G	L	A	N	D		G	
I	M	P	E	L	S		G		I	C	E	S
N				O			E		N		T	
G	A	R	A	G	E		D	I	G	E	S	T
	U		W		R			R				E
I	S	L	E		R		S	E	A	N	C	E
	T		S	T	A	K	E		B			T
H	E	R	O		N		X		H	I	V	E
	R		M	I	D	G	E		O			R
H	E	R	E		S		S	C	R	E	W	S

120

C	A	L	A	M	A	R	I		J	U	N	K
U			S		V		N		A			E
D	O	C	K		O	P	T	I	C	I	A	N
G			E		I		O		K			N
E	R	O	D	E	D		N		E			E
L		N		A		M	E	N	T	H	O	L
		T		C		A		O		A		
F	R	O	T	H	E	D		S		G		A
E			O		S		C	E	A	S	E	D
N			M		S		A		S			U
C	A	R	A	V	A	N	S		S	I	L	L
E			T		Y		T		E			T
S	I	L	O		S	W	E	L	T	E	R	S

121

L	I	G	H	T		O		F		A		C
I			O		E	V	E	R	Y	D	A	Y
F	I	E	L	D		E		I		V		G
T			D	E	P	R	E	S	S	I	O	N
E		H		C				K		S		E
D	R	A	M	A	T	I	C		G	A	I	T
		R		Y		L		J		B		
P	E	A	L		F	L	O	O	D	L	I	T
I		S		C				I		E		E
M	I	S	H	E	A	R	I	N	G			A
P		I		D		A		T	H	U	G	S
L	E	N	I	E	N	C	E		E			E
E		G		S		E		H	E	W	E	D

122

M	U	T	A	T	E	D		W	I	P	E	D
I			F			R		I		A		U
S		P	L	A	C	A	R	D		L		E
S			O			G		E	N	A	C	T
P	A	G	A	N	S		N			C		
E			T		T	R	O	U	S	E	R	S
N		C			E		I			S		U
T	R	A	W	L	E	R	S		W			N
		R			L		Y	E	A	R	N	S
A	U	R	A	L		P			F			H
X		I		O	R	A	N	G	E	S		I
L		E		S		L			R			N
E	E	R	I	E		M	A	S	S	I	V	E

123

C	I	C	A	D	A		E		S	E	W	N
H			M	N	A	V	E	L			I	
E	L	S	E		K		I		E	T	C	H
C			N		L	A	C	E	D		K	
K	I	N	D	L	E		T		G	R	E	W
E				E			E		E		T	
R	A	S	C	A	L		D	E	S	I	S	T
	B		A		U		E					I
A	S	P	S		M		F	L	A	W	E	D
	C		T	A	B	L	E		N			I
P	O	L	L		A		E		V	A	S	E
	N		E	D	G	E	D		I			S
O	D	E	S		O		S	I	L	E	N	T

124

A	S	S	A	S	S	I	N		H	O	O	D
S			S		H		E		E			A
P	I	N	K		Y	E	A	R	L	I	N	G
I			E		L		R		I			G
R	U	N	W	A	Y		E		U			E
E		U		F		G	R	A	M	M	A	R
		D		A		U		I		A		
Q	U	E	E	R	L	Y		D		I		C
U			D		E		K	E	E	N	E	R
E			I		V		I		L			E
N	I	M	B	L	E	S	T		A	R	I	A
C			L		L		E		T			T
H	O	P	E		S	U	S	P	E	N	S	E

125

J	U	M	B	O		S		F		D		E
U			R		S	H	E	A	R	E	R	S
T	W	E	A	K		A		I		D		T
T			S	U	M	M	E	R	T	I	M	E
E		S		D				S		C		E
D	I	P	L	O	M	A	T		M	A	I	M
		I		S		P		C		T		
L	E	N	T		R	E	T	R	I	E	V	E
A		E		S				A		S		J
W	I	L	D	E	R	N	E	S	S			E
Y		E		A		O		H	A	V	O	C
E	A	S	E	M	E	N	T		R			T
R		S		S		E		P	I	O	U	S

126

E	S	C	A	P	E	D		Y	E	A	R	S
M			V			R		O		B		L
I		S	E	T	B	A	C	K		S		A
G			N			M		E	N	T	R	Y
R	E	F	U	N	D		P			A		
A			E		R	O	A	D	S	I	D	E
N		I			E		N			N		N
T	U	G	B	O	A	T	S		F			T
		U			M		Y	E	L	L	O	W
A	W	A	K	E		O			U			I
J		N		N	I	B	B	L	E	D		N
A		A		V		O			N			E
R	U	S	T	Y		E	M	P	T	I	E	D

127

F	L	O	A	T	S		P		W	A	R	Y
L			I		E	V	A	D	E		E	
A	T	O	M		L		R		S	E	A	L
S			E		L	E	A	P	T		L	
H	O	R	D	E	S		S		E	D	I	T
E				B			O		R		G	
S	C	R	U	B	S		L	I	N	I	N	G
	O		P		C			C				O
S	N	A	G		A		B	Y	P	A	S	S
	Q		R	E	B	E	L		A			S
T	U	B	A		I		A		S	E	M	I
	E		D	R	E	A	D		T			P
T	R	E	E		S		E	X	A	C	T	S

128

N	O	W	A	D	A	Y	S		I	D	L	E
U			U		C		T		M			N
M	I	N	D		O	V	E	R	A	W	E	D
B			I		R		R		G			O
L	A	G	O	O	N		E		E			W
Y		I		U		L	O	O	S	E	N	S
		S		S		A		N		L		
R	O	T	A	T	E	D		C		K		H
U			L		N		M	E	A	S	L	Y
N			I		T		O		D			P
N	U	M	B	E	R	E	D		M	Y	T	H
E			I		A		E		I			E
R	A	P	S		P	O	S	I	T	I	O	N

129

N	O	T	C	H		G		E		M		L
I			R		M	O	S	Q	U	I	T	O
P	L	E	A	D		N		U		M		D
P			B	A	R	G	A	I	N	I	N	G
L		B		I				P		C		E
E	N	A	B	L	I	N	G		S	K	I	D
		R		Y		U		P		I		
J	O	B	S		U	N	E	A	R	N	E	D
E		E		C				Y		G		E
S	O	C	I	A	L	I	T	E	S			F
T		U		N		R		E	A	G	L	E
E	L	E	V	A	T	O	R		W			N
R		D		L		N		K	N	E	A	D

130

A	Q	U	A	T	I	C		F	E	R	A	L
C			L			L		I		U		E
O		G	L	O	W	E	R	S		N		F
U			U			F		H	E	A	R	T
S	H	A	R	E	D		T			W		
T			E		E	V	A	L	U	A	T	E
I		C			L		I			Y		N
C	H	A	P	L	A	I	N		D			C
		B			Y		T	R	A	U	M	A
N	O	B	L	Y		P			N			M
O		A		E	L	A	S	T	I	C		P
D		G		L		I			E			E
S	T	E	E	P		R	E	P	L	I	E	D

131

F	I	Z	Z	L	E		S		U	S	E	D
A			E		N	I	C	E	R		M	
L	A	M	B		E		A		C	U	B	S
L			R		M	U	L	C	H		R	
I	N	F	A	M	Y		P		I	D	O	L
N				I			E		N		I	
G	A	L	A	X	Y		L	A	S	T	L	Y
	L		N		O			S				I
H	A	L	O		U		W	H	E	E	Z	E
	R		I	N	N	E	R		R			L
O	M	E	N		G		I		A	G	E	D
	E		T	I	E	R	S		S			E
A	D	D	S		R		T	E	E	M	E	D

132

T	H	R	E	A	T	E	N		M	O	N	O
A			L		H		O		E			R
T	A	C	O		A	G	R	E	E	I	N	G
T			P		I		M		K			A
O	R	D	E	R	S		A		L			N
O		U		E		P	L	A	Y	E	R	S
		N		A		O		W		A		
J	U	G	G	L	E	D		R		S		T
O			Y		L		O	Y	S	T	E	R
I			R		U		L		U			A
S	T	R	A	N	D	E	D		P	O	N	D
T			T		E		E		E			E
S	O	M	E		S	U	N	D	R	I	E	S

133

Y	A	C	H	T		S		B		D		S
E			E		I	N	C	I	D	E	N	T
L	I	L	A	C		O		L		S		I
L			D	I	A	B	O	L	I	C	A	L
E		C		T				S		R		T
D	E	A	F	E	N	E	D		R	I	D	S
		T		S		W		M		B		
A	L	A	S		S	E	D	A	T	E	L	Y
I		M		W				X		S		O
S	E	A	M	A	N	S	H	I	P			D
L		R		R		H		M	E	R	G	E
E	X	A	M	P	L	E	S			E		L
S		N		S		D		F	L	A	N	S

134

P	O	L	L	U	T	E		T	I	A	R	A
A			I			S		I		N		N
C		S	N	O	O	P	E	D		Y		E
I			E			Y		E	L	B	O	W
F	I	B	U	L	A		P			O		
I			P		S	H	E	E	P	D	O	G
E		E			T		T			Y		O
D	E	A	D	L	I	N	E		C			U
		N			R		R	E	A	P	E	R
T	R	A	S	H		F			M			M
A		T		A	M	A	S	S	E	D		E
U		I		T		N			R			T
T	U	C	K	S		G	R	E	A	S	E	S

135

J	A	G	G	E	D		P		G	A	P	S
U			E		A	D	A	G	E		R	
N	A	P	E		R		R		I	T	E	M
I			S		T	E	A	M	S		F	
O	W	N	E	R	S		G		H	E	A	L
R				Y			O		A		C	
S	A	U	C	E	S		N	E	S	T	E	D
	P		U		T		R					E
S	P	A	R		R		R	A	C	I	S	M
	E		T	R	A	C	E		R			A
G	A	L	A		Y		U		Y	A	W	N
	S		I	D	E	A	S		P			D
C	E	L	L		D		E	X	T	O	L	S

136

A	C	Q	U	A	I	N	T		E	V	I	L
D			N		N		R		M			E
V	O	I	D		G	R	A	B	B	I	N	G
E			U		O		V		E			A
R	E	C	E	N	T		E		R			C
B		U		O		C	L	O	S	E	L	Y
		P		D		O		P		W		
I	N	S	P	E	C	T		E		E		C
N			A		O		E	N	E	R	G	Y
F			R		N		A		L			C
E	N	H	A	N	C	E	S		V	E	I	L
R			D		U		E		E			E
S	A	F	E		R	E	S	I	S	T	E	D

SOLUTIONS

137

K	N	I	F	E		S		O		D		S
O			A		S	T	I	F	F	E	S	T
S	T	A	M	P		U		F		F		A
H			E	L	O	N	G	A	T	I	N	G
E		P		U				L		A		E
R	E	A	R	M	O	S	T		A	N	T	S
		R		S		K		S		T		
G	R	A	M		D	I	S	A	B	L	E	D
U		M		A				D		Y		I
N	E	E	D	L	E	S	S	L	Y			T
M		D		L		I		Y	O	U	T	H
E	M	I	N	E	N	C	E		U			E
N		C		Y		K		P	R	I	O	R

138

C	O	N	C	E	A	L		J	E	A	N	S
O			R			E		U		L		A
N		N	I	G	G	A	R	D		M		P
C			T			F		O	K	A	Y	S
E	N	T	I	R	E		L			N		
D			C		D	R	A	W	B	A	C	K
E		A			G		S			C		N
D	E	C	I	B	E	L	S		M			E
		C			S		O	P	A	Q	U	E
B	L	U	E	S		B			S			L
U		S		U	N	L	E	A	S	H		I
F		E		E		U			E			N
F	A	D	E	D		R	E	A	D	I	N	G

139

A	C	H	I	N	G		G		N	A	Y	S
S			C		O	R	A	T	E		A	
P	O	L	O		O		R		S	I	N	K
E			N		D	R	A	F	T		K	
C	H	A	S	E	S		G		L	O	I	N
T				R			E		E		N	
S	A	F	A	R	I		D	O	S	A	G	E
	I		R		N			V				S
T	R	O	D		S		H	A	B	I	T	S
	C		U	N	I	T	E		I			E
T	R	I	O		G		I		N	E	O	N
	E		U	S	H	E	R		G			C
O	W	L	S		T		S	W	E	R	V	E

140

H	A	Z	A	R	D	E	D		E	Y	E	D
A			M		R		I		X			Y
T	O	G	A		I	M	M	A	T	U	R	E
R			Z		E		P		E			I
E	M	B	E	D	S		L		N			N
D		L		O		N	E	E	D	I	N	G
		O		T		O		X		N		
A	N	C	I	E	N	T		A		K		A
P			N		E		A	M	U	S	E	D
A			B		I		U		L			H
T	H	R	O	N	G	E	D		C	O	M	E
H			R		H		I		E			R
Y	A	R	N		S	A	T	U	R	A	T	E

141

A	R	R	A	Y		A		L		I		S
W			R		I	N	W	A	R	D	L	Y
H	E	N	C	E		T		R		E		S
I			S	A	U	E	R	K	R	A	U	T
L		O		R				S		L		E
E	M	B	A	L	M	E	R		F	I	R	M
		S		Y		V		H		S		
L	O	C	K		P	E	D	A	N	T	I	C
O		E		O				I		S		U
B	I	N	O	C	U	L	A	R	S			S
B		I		E		O		S	P	U	R	T
E	N	T	R	A	I	L	S		A			O
D		Y		N		L		P	S	A	L	M

142

L	O	B	B	I	E	S		F	O	L	L	Y
I			E			P		A		O		A
G		S	T	E	W	A	R	D		C		M
A			R			R		S	W	A	B	S
M	O	S	A	I	C		B			T		
E			Y		E	V	A	C	U	E	E	S
N		M			D		L			D		U
T	R	A	C	K	E	R	S		R			B
		L			D		A	B	A	S	E	D
P	L	A	Z	A		T			I			U
U		R		C	H	I	M	I	N	G		I
M		I		R		F			E			N
P	H	A	S	E		F	O	R	D	I	N	G

143

L	O	C	A	L	S		S		B	E	A	U
E			R		T	A	P	E	R		C	
T	O	N	E		U		R		I	T	C	H
T			N		D	R	A	P	E		L	
U	N	E	A	S	Y		W		F	E	A	T
C				E			L		E		I	
E	A	S	I	E	R		S	C	R	I	M	P
	T		M		A			O				A
C	H	O	P		B		A	B	A	T	E	S
	E		O	R	B	I	T		C			T
P	I	E	R		I		O		T	I	R	E
	S		T	O	T	A	L		E			L
A	M	P	S		S		L	A	D	L	E	S

144

M	A	G	N	A	T	E	S		M	A	M	A
O			Y		I		T		E			S
D	O	L	L		L	E	A	K	A	G	E	S
E			O		E		P		N			E
M	O	A	N	E	D		L		E			T
S		C		M		H	E	A	R	S	E	S
		I		I		A		L		O		
U	P	D	A	T	E	D		T		O		U
N			T		E		H	O	R	N	E	T
E			T		R		Y		A			T
V	O	L	A	T	I	L	E		M	A	D	E
E			C		E		N		P			R
N	I	C	K		R	E	A	S	S	E	S	S

SOLUTIONS

145

S	W	E	A	R		S		I		A		F
P			N		S	K	Y	D	I	V	E	R
I	D	I	O	M		I		E		O		A
R			N	E	U	T	R	A	L	I	T	Y
A		J		A				S		D		E
L	E	A	R	N	I	N	G		S	A	I	D
		C		S		E		H		B		
I	R	K	S		M	E	T	A	L	L	I	C
N		K		O				V		E		H
L	A	N	D	S	C	A	P	E	S			E
A		I		C		P		N	A	I	V	E
I	N	F	L	A	T	E	D		L			S
D		E		R		S		S	T	Y	L	E

146

W	I	Z	A	R	D	S		K	O	A	L	A
A			F			O		I		D		M
T		E	F	F	E	C	T	S		V		I
E			E			K		S	C	A	L	D
R	E	S	C	U	E		L			N		
I			T		V	I	A	D	U	C	T	S
N		M			I		U			E		P
G	R	I	M	A	C	E	D		C			E
		H			T		S	T	A	T	I	C
K	N	A	V	E		P			V			K
I		C		A	B	A	S	H	E	D		L
T		L		R		N			R			E
E	V	E	N	S		T	H	A	N	K	E	D

147

L	I	Z	A	R	D		G		O	R	B	S
O			R		W	H	A	R	F		R	
V	E	T	O		A		R		F	L	A	K
A			M		R	O	B	E	S		I	
B	E	H	A	L	F		A		E	E	L	S
L				E			G		I		L	
E	C	L	A	I	R		E	N	S	U	E	D
	O		M		O			U				O
K	N	O	B		M		E	T	C	H	E	D
	S		L	L	A	M	A		R			D
M	I	N	I		N		V		U	R	G	E
	S		N	I	C	H	E		M			R
S	T	A	G		E		S	U	B	T	L	Y

148

H	E	R	A	L	D	E	D		L	O	A	F
O			I		E		O		E			I
T	O	L	D		T	A	M	P	E	R	E	D
E			E		E		I		R			G
L	E	N	D	E	R		N		E			E
S		U		V		C	O	L	D	E	S	T
		M		E		R		O		A		
P	U	B	E	R	T	Y		S		R		A
U			N		I		F	E	A	S	T	S
S			C		C		U		S			H
H	I	J	A	C	K	E	D		S	U	M	O
E			S		E		G		E			R
D	U	P	E		T	R	E	A	S	U	R	E

149

W	O	M	A	N		J		B		B		A
A			L		R	E	P	A	I	R	E	R
G	L	U	E	D		S		G		A		I
O			S	Y	N	T	H	E	T	I	C	S
N		O		K				L		N		E
S	U	B	M	E	R	G	E		S	I	G	N
		T		S		A		S		E		
N	E	A	R		A	B	A	C	U	S	E	S
U		I		S				A		T		E
D	I	N	N	E	R	W	A	R	E			A
I		I		D		E		Y	A	R	D	S
T	E	N	T	A	C	L	E		T			O
Y		G		N		D		A	S	H	E	N

150

T	W	E	A	K	E	D		V	I	G	I	L
R			W			E		A		L		U
I		H	A	I	R	C	U	T		O		T
M			R			K		S	N	A	K	E
M	E	N	D	E	D		R			T		
L			S		W	R	A	P	P	E	R	S
S		S			E		I			D		H
T	R	A	M	P	L	E	D		D			O
		M			T		S	E	A	L	E	D
T	A	P	E	D		C			N			D
H		L		I	T	A	L	I	C	S		I
E		E		A		R			E			E
M	E	D	A	L		T	A	R	D	I	E	R

151

G	R	E	A	S	Y		P		N	A	B	S
I			D		E	L	I	T	E		E	
D	O	D	O		A		R		A	L	S	O
D			R		R	E	A	C	T		I	
I	N	T	E	R	N		N		E	N	D	S
E				U			H		S		E	
R	A	V	A	G	E		A	R	T	I	S	T
	R		L		L			O				R
O	M	I	T		E		F	E	E	B	L	E
	R		E	X	C	E	L		N			M
D	E	A	R		T		O		J	A	M	B
	S		E	P	E	E	S		O			L
S	T	U	D		D		S	C	Y	T	H	E

152

H	A	R	A	N	G	U	E		V	I	S	A
E			N		A		N		O			B
D	A	W	N		L	E	A	N	I	N	G	S
G			U		E		M		C			U
E	X	I	L	E	S		E		E			R
S		N		A		F	L	A	S	H	E	D
		T		R		A		B		I		
B	O	O	K	L	E	T		B		N		D
U			A		N		G	A	R	T	E	R
S			R		T		U		A			I
H	E	X	A	G	O	N	S		V	E	A	L
E			T		M		T		E			L
S	A	N	E		B	R	O	A	D	E	N	S

SOLUTIONS

153

H	U	M	A	N		S		S		S		A
U			U		S	T	O	P	P	E	R	S
B	L	A	N	K		U		O		M		T
B			T	A	M	B	O	U	R	I	N	E
L		W		Y				T		C		R
E	M	A	N	A	T	E	S		S	O	W	N
		L		K		R		I		L		
T	A	L	K		R	E	A	C	T	O	R	S
I		P		S				I		N		O
P	H	A	R	M	A	C	I	E	S			R
T		P		E		H		R	A	C	E	D
O	V	E	R	A	W	E	S		G			I
E		R		R		W		F	A	K	E	D

154

B	E	L	A	T	E	D		C	I	D	E	R
U			B			U		E		Y		O
L		M	O	I	S	T	E	N		N		L
L			A			Y		T	R	A	D	E
Y	E	A	R	L	Y		L			M		
I			D		E	X	A	C	T	I	N	G
N		N			L		P			C		R
G	R	A	N	U	L	E	S		C			A
		M			S		E	R	A	S	E	D
D	R	I	N	K		T			J			U
U		B		E	V	A	S	I	O	N		A
B		I		E		L			L			T
S	N	A	I	L		C	A	Y	E	N	N	E

155

M	E	N	A	C	E		O		D	U	A	L
O			M		R	A	B	B	I		M	
B	U	L	B		U		L		F	U	M	E
S			E		P	R	O	O	F		O	
T	U	R	R	E	T		N		U	R	N	S
E				G			G		S		I	
R	A	N	D	O	M		S	E	E	S	A	W
	D		I		A			L				A
H	U	L	A		N		S	K	A	T	E	D
	L		R	E	A	C	H		W			D
T	A	X	I		G		A		F	E	L	L
	T		E	M	E	N	D		U			E
L	E	S	S		R		Y	E	L	P	E	D

156

K	N	E	A	D	I	N	G		Q	U	A	D
E			D		R		L		U			I
T	U	N	A		A	M	A	T	E	U	R	S
T			P		T		N		U			O
L	O	A	T	H	E		C		E			W
E		U		E		H	E	A	D	M	A	N
		R		R		I		N		O		
M	E	A	D	O	W	S		T		D		A
A			E		A		S	I	N	E	W	S
S			A		R		O		O			I
K	I	N	D	L	I	E	R		B	O	L	D
E			E		E		T		L			E
D	O	W	N		R	E	S	P	E	C	T	S

157

P	E	T	A	L		S		C		O		C
R			R		U	N	L	A	W	F	U	L
O	U	N	C	E		U		I		F		O
P			H	A	M	B	U	R	G	E	R	S
E		M		R				O		R		E
L	E	A	N	N	E	S	S		B	I	N	D
		N		S		E		C		N		
N	A	G	S		S	T	R	A	I	G	H	T
I		R		E				C		S		R
C	O	O	R	D	I	N	A	T	E			A
E		V		I		E		I	C	I	N	G
S	K	E	T	C	H	E	S		H			I
T		S		T		D		T	O	X	I	C

158

H	O	S	T	I	L	E		R	E	A	L	M
A			H			R		I		B		E
N		A	R	C	H	A	I	C		R		L
D			O			S		E	X	A	L	T
C	O	B	W	E	B		T			D		
U			N		L	E	A	F	L	E	T	S
F		F			O		S			S		E
F	R	A	G	R	A	N	T		E			N
		N			T		Y	A	C	H	T	S
R	E	A	R	S		K			Z			U
O		T		L	A	N	K	I	E	R		O
A		I		A		O			M			U
R	E	C	A	P		W	R	E	A	T	H	S

159

P	A	L	A	C	E		B		G	I	G	S
I			L		W	H	A	L	E		A	
V	E	R	B		E		N		L	E	W	D
O			U		R	E	D	I	D		K	
T	H	U	M	B	S		A		I	R	I	S
E				O			G		N		N	
D	A	M	A	G	E		E	N	G	A	G	E
	N		F		L			I				N
H	A	L	F		E		F	L	U	T	E	S
	T		A	N	G	E	L		P			L
B	O	M	B		A		U		P	U	M	A
	M		L	U	N	G	E		E			V
H	Y	P	E		T		S	A	D	D	L	E

160

R	E	P	A	R	T	E	E		I	N	C	H
A			I		I		A		N			U
I	O	N	S		D	E	S	I	S	T	E	D
S			L		E		I		I			D
I	D	L	E	R	S		N		S			L
N		A		E		A	G	I	T	A	T	E
		M		S		I		C		C		
Q	U	A	R	T	E	R		O		H		O
U			E		D		U	N	B	E	N	D
E			P		G		S		O			D
L	A	X	A	T	I	V	E		N	O	T	E
L			I		E		R		E			S
S	H	O	D		R	E	S	I	D	E	N	T

161

G	H	O	U	L		L		R		M		S
A			N		B	A	S	E	M	E	N	T
M	I	N	D	S		V		F		A		O
B			O	C	C	A	S	I	O	N	A	L
O		B		U				T		W		E
L	E	A	P	F	R	O	G		T	H	E	N
		R		F		A		S		I		
M	O	B	S		S	K	I	T	T	L	E	S
O		E		B				U		E		U
U	N	C	H	A	N	G	I	N	G			D
R		U		W		U		T	A	X	E	D
N	E	E	D	L	E	S	S		F			E
S		S		S		T		O	F	T	E	N

162

U	N	T	A	M	E	D		C	A	M	E	L
T			P			R		I		U		E
E		A	P	P	O	I	N	T		M		E
N			E			P		E	M	B	E	R
S	T	R	A	T	A		K			L		
I			L		I	N	N	O	C	E	N	T
L		S			L		E			S		H
S	T	A	M	P	E	D	E		B			R
		W			D		S	T	A	B	L	E
T	E	M	P	O		H			N			A
E		I		A	N	A	G	R	A	M		D
R		L		T		L			N			E
M	E	L	T	S		T	R	E	A	T	E	D

163

A	B	S	O	R	B		A		A	W	A	Y
N			B		E	M	B	E	D		U	
G	A	Z	E		N		O		J	A	C	K
L			S		C	E	L	L	O		T	
E	N	M	E	S	H		I		U	N	I	T
R				A			S		R		O	
S	A	V	A	G	E		H	O	N	I	N	G
	L		B		N			U				A
R	I	N	D		V		S	T	R	O	L	L
	M		O	P	E	R	A		O			L
F	O	A	M		L		F		M	E	M	O
	N		E	V	O	K	E		P			N
H	Y	M	N		P		S	A	S	H	E	S

164

D	I	V	U	L	G	E	D		K	I	N	G
R			P		I		E		N			A
I	N	N	S		R	E	A	L	I	S	T	S
F			E		T		L		G			K
T	H	A	T	C	H		E		H			E
S		R		O		P	R	O	T	E	S	T
		T		I		A		G		R		
N	E	S	T	L	E	D		L		R		F
U			H		N		W	E	A	S	E	L
M			I		R		A		B			A
B	L	E	E	D	I	N	G		B	A	R	K
E			V		C		E		O			E
R	I	P	E		H	E	R	E	T	I	C	S

165

M	E	T	A	L		C		A		S		E
E			X		S	H	A	D	O	W	E	D
M	I	M	I	C		I		D		E		I
B			S	E	T	T	L	E	M	E	N	T
E		J		D				D		T		E
R	E	A	W	A	K	E	N		D	E	E	D
		Y		R		G		W		N		
V	O	W	S		U	G	L	I	N	E	S	S
E		A		A				D		D		H
I	L	L	E	G	A	L	I	T	Y			A
L		K		A		I		H	A	T	E	D
E	Y	E	L	I	N	E	R		N			E
D		R		N		S		S	K	I	E	D

166

E	L	E	G	A	N	T		B	A	S	I	C
X			E			I		O		Q		O
T		I	N	S	U	L	I	N		U		P
E			I			E		D	R	A	K	E
R	E	M	A	N	D		C			R		
N			L		R	E	A	P	P	E	A	R
A		P			I		U			S		E
L	E	A	R	N	E	R	S		T			L
		R			R		E	N	A	B	L	E
G	U	A	V	A		C			N			V
L		D		I	M	A	G	I	N	E		A
I		O		M		K			E			N
B	O	X	E	S		E	V	I	D	E	N	T

167

M	A	I	L	E	D		D		A	S	K	S
I			I		Y	E	A	S	T		I	
N	O	R	M		I		W		T	A	C	T
U			B		N	U	D	G	E		K	
T	H	R	O	N	G		L		N	A	I	L
E				O			E		D		N	
S	A	L	A	D	S		D	E	S	I	G	N
	D		U		H			K				O
S	M	O	G		O		G	E	R	A	R	D
	I		M	A	C	H	U		A			U
T	R	U	E		K		E		K	I	L	L
	A		N	E	E	D	S		E			E
F	L	A	T		D		T	O	S	S	E	S

168

E	S	C	A	L	A	T	E		W	O	O	D
X			L		R		L		O			E
C	O	W	L		M	E	A	T	B	A	L	L
U			O		E		I		B			A
S	E	A	T	E	D		E		L			Y
E		K		V		E	S	T	E	E	M	S
		I		E		L		W		X		
S	Y	N	O	N	Y	M		I		I		H
A			U		O		K	N	O	T	T	Y
U			T		U		A		A			E
N	A	R	R	A	T	O	R		S	C	A	N
A			U		H		M		I			A
S	P	I	N		S	O	A	P	S	U	D	S

169

N	E	P	A	L	■	H	■	J	■	D	■	L
A	■	■	B	■	R	E	H	E	A	R	S	E
U	N	F	E	D	■	R	■	S	■	A	■	A
S	■	■	T	A	P	E	S	T	R	I	E	S
E	■	D	■	I	■	■	■	S	■	N	■	E
A	M	A	S	S	I	N	G	■	S	P	E	D
■	■	R	■	Y	■	O	■	G	■	I	■	■
A	P	E	D	■	T	R	I	U	M	P	H	S
N	■	D	■	C	■	■	■	A	■	E	■	W
N	E	E	D	L	E	W	O	R	K	■	■	A
U	■	V	■	E	■	E	■	D	I	N	G	Y
A	M	I	C	A	B	L	Y	■	L	■	■	E
L	■	L	■	N	■	L	■	S	T	A	I	D

170

C	A	N	A	S	T	A	■	V	O	C	A	L
A	■	■	D	■	■	X	■	O	■	E	■	I
T	■	O	V	E	R	E	A	T	■	R	■	D
E	■	■	E	■	■	D	■	E	X	A	M	S
G	L	A	R	E	D	■	S	■	■	M	■	■
O	■	■	B	■	A	W	A	R	D	I	N	G
R	■	A	■	■	T	■	L	■	■	C	■	U
Y	O	U	N	G	E	S	T	■	R	■	■	I
■	■	D	■	■	S	■	S	C	A	R	E	D
S	K	I	M	P	■	I	■	■	N	■	■	A
E	■	T	■	E	M	B	R	A	C	E	■	N
E	■	E	■	R	■	I	■	■	I	■	■	C
M	A	D	A	M	■	S	A	R	D	I	N	E

171

L	O	C	A	T	E	■	O	■	W	I	N	G
O	■	■	B	■	J	U	R	O	R	■	E	■
Y	O	G	A	■	E	■	G	■	O	P	A	L
A	■	■	S	■	C	H	A	I	N	■	R	■
L	A	T	E	S	T	■	N	■	G	L	E	E
T	■	■	■	U	■	■	I	■	E	■	S	■
Y	A	W	N	E	D	■	C	A	D	E	T	S
■	N	■	E	■	I	■	■	R	■	■	■	L
T	Y	P	E	■	S	■	I	C	I	C	L	E
■	T	■	D	I	C	E	D	■	M	■	■	I
H	I	L	L	■	U	■	O	■	P	R	I	G
■	M	■	E	A	S	E	L	■	E	■	■	H
K	E	Y	S	■	S	■	S	O	L	V	E	S

172

P	L	A	N	N	E	R	S	■	S	U	V	A
A	■	■	I	■	R	■	T	■	M	■	■	S
S	A	V	E	■	O	R	A	T	I	O	N	S
T	■	■	C	■	D	■	R	■	L	■	■	E
R	E	C	E	D	E	■	V	■	E	■	■	S
Y	■	A	■	I	■	R	E	A	D	E	R	S
■	■	M	■	N	■	A	■	B	■	A	■	■
K	E	E	N	E	S	T	■	L	■	C	■	B
I	■	■	E	■	E	■	L	E	C	H	E	R
T	■	■	G	■	R	■	O	■	A	■	■	A
T	R	E	A	D	I	N	G	■	R	O	C	K
E	■	■	T	■	E	■	I	■	V	■	■	E
N	I	N	E	■	S	I	C	K	E	N	E	D

173

V	I	S	A	S	■	D	■	A	■	P	■	G
A	■	■	D	■	A	R	M	C	H	A	I	R
G	R	E	E	D	■	A	■	U	■	P	■	A
U	■	■	N	A	U	G	H	T	I	E	S	T
E	■	O	■	L	■	■	■	E	■	R	■	E
R	E	B	E	L	L	E	D	■	A	W	E	D
■	■	E	■	Y	■	E	■	A	■	O	■	■
D	O	D	O	■	E	L	E	C	T	R	I	C
A	■	I	■	P	■	■	■	R	■	K	■	E
W	H	E	E	L	C	H	A	I	R	■	■	R
N	■	N	■	E	■	O	■	D	A	N	C	E
E	X	C	H	A	N	G	E	■	M	■	■	A
D	■	E	■	S	■	S	■	S	P	I	E	L

174

T	R	E	A	S	O	N	■	T	E	A	C	H
R	■	■	M	■	■	E	■	O	■	N	■	E
A	■	F	O	R	G	A	V	E	■	T	■	R
N	■	■	R	■	■	T	■	S	T	A	T	E
Q	U	E	A	S	Y	■	P	■	■	C	■	■
U	■	■	L	■	A	W	A	I	T	I	N	G
I	■	U	■	■	R	■	U	■	■	D	■	R
L	E	M	M	I	N	G	S	■	C	■	■	U
■	■	P	■	■	S	■	E	V	A	D	E	D
T	R	I	E	D	■	S	■	■	R	■	■	G
E	■	R	■	E	N	T	R	I	E	S	■	I
N	■	E	■	F	■	O	■	■	E	■	■	N
T	E	D	D	Y	■	W	E	A	R	I	N	G

175

E	X	P	E	L	S	■	S	■	O	R	A	L
T	■	■	E	■	N	E	E	D	Y	■	B	■
C	H	A	R	■	A	■	N	■	S	W	A	N
H	■	■	I	■	G	R	A	F	T	■	N	■
I	N	T	E	R	S	■	T	■	E	D	D	Y
N	■	■	■	I	■	■	O	■	R	■	O	■
G	A	R	A	G	E	■	R	E	S	E	N	T
■	L	■	L	■	N	■	■	M	■	■	■	A
S	C	A	B	■	H	■	T	U	B	E	R	S
■	O	■	I	N	A	N	E	■	L	■	■	S
O	V	E	N	■	N	■	A	■	I	S	L	E
■	E	■	O	C	C	U	R	■	N	■	■	L
A	S	P	S	■	E	■	S	I	D	L	E	S

176

J	O	S	T	L	I	N	G	■	Y	A	R	D
O	■	■	E	■	N	■	L	■	E	■	■	U
Y	O	K	E	■	S	E	A	F	A	R	E	R
O	■	■	T	■	E	■	N	■	R	■	■	E
U	P	S	H	O	T	■	C	■	N	■	■	S
S	■	O	■	V	■	C	E	N	S	O	R	S
■	■	D	■	A	■	O	■	U	■	G	■	■
T	R	A	I	L	E	D	■	L	■	R	■	U
E	■	■	N	■	N	■	U	L	C	E	R	S
T	■	■	S	■	T	■	N	■	Y	■	■	E
H	A	S	T	I	E	S	T	■	C	A	L	F
E	■	■	E	■	R	■	I	■	L	■	■	U
R	U	M	P	■	S	K	E	L	E	T	A	L

177

J	U	I	C	E		W		S		T		P
A			O		C	O	R	P	O	R	A	L
B	O	A	T	S		K		A		E		A
B			S	U	P	E	R	S	T	A	R	S
E		N		G				M		S		M
D	R	A	M	A	T	I	C		T	U	B	A
		V		R		R		W		R		
S	A	I	L		R	E	C	O	V	E	R	S
U		G		C				R		D		O
C	H	A	R	A	C	T	E	R	S			U
K		T		R		O		Y	E	A	R	S
E	M	E	N	D	I	N	G		A			E
D		D		S		S		E	M	B	E	D

178

U	N	B	L	O	C	K		I	N	A	P	T
N			I			N		U		I		A
C		E	M	I	N	E	N	T		T		L
O			B			W		A	B	A	T	E
V	E	N	E	E	R		A			C		
E			R		U	N	C	O	R	K	E	D
R		H			P		R			S		O
S	E	A	P	L	A	N	E		F			M
		N			L		S	T	A	N	C	E
A	I	D	E	S		V			C			S
B		L		N	U	A	N	C	E	S		T
U		E		O		N			T			I
T	H	R	O	W		S	E	I	S	M	I	C

179

N	O	V	E	L	S		S		W	I	P	E
O			B		U	N	C	L	E		R	
B	A	R	B		I		R		T	E	A	M
L			E		T	R	A	I	N		I	
E	X	O	D	U	S		P		E	A	R	N
S				R			E		S		I	
T	A	L	E	N	T		D	A	S	H	E	D
	B		L		R			N				I
C	U	R	B		A		I	D	E	A	L	S
	S		O	F	F	E	R		X			C
V	I	E	W		F		K		A	R	E	A
	V		E	X	I	L	E		C			R
M	E	N	D		C		D	O	T	T	E	D

180

V	A	C	A	T	I	N	G		B	I	T	F
A			P		D		O		E			D
U	L	N	A		L	E	A	S	H	I	N	G
L			R		E		T		E			I
T	E	S	T	E	D		E		L			N
S		A		L		V	E	N	D	I	N	G
		G		S		E		O		D		
E	L	E	M	E	N	T		U		E		S
R			I		A		E	N	C	A	M	P
A			D		T		I		A			A
S	E	E	D	L	I	N	G		B	E	A	D
E			L		V		H		L			E
S	I	Z	E		E	X	T	R	E	M	E	S

181

A	L	I	B	I		Y		A		S		S
F			E		H	E	I	G	H	T	E	N
F	I	N	A	L		T		O		I		E
O			M	A	R	I	O	N	E	T	T	E
R		M		D				Y		C		Z
D	I	A	B	E	T	I	C		S	H	O	E
		I		N		M		F		I		
S	E	N	D		S	P	R	A	I	N	E	D
O		T		M				L		G		O
L	E	A	D	E	R	L	E	S	S			O
E		I		T		A		E	A	S	E	D
L	E	N	I	E	N	C	Y		T			L
Y		S		R		K		M	E	L	E	E

182

E	X	E	C	U	T	E		H	A	T	C	H
X			I			P		U		O		O
O		D	I	S	M	I	S	S		W		E
R			N			C		H	E	A	R	D
C	A	P	I	T	A		W			R		
I			C		C	H	A	R	A	D	E	S
S		N			H		I			S		C
M	E	E	K	N	E	S	S		L			R
		T			D		T	R	A	U	M	A
K	E	B	A	B		O			Y			P
I		A		I	M	B	I	B	E	D		P
D		L		R		O			R			E
S	O	L	I	D		E	X	I	S	T	E	D

183

O	R	N	A	M	E	N	T		B	U	L	L
R			D		L		A		A			E
P	O	N	D		O	R	B	I	T	I	N	G
H			L		P		L		T			E
A	P	I	E	C	E		E		L			N
N		C		R		U	S	H	E	R	E	D
		E		A		O		I		U		
D	I	S	A	B	L	E		G		S		U
R			T		A		S	H	R	E	W	D
O			T		P		L		O			D
O	R	N	A	T	E	L	Y		P	A	R	E
P			I		L		E		E			R
S	P	A	N		S	T	R	E	S	S	E	S

184

F	I	N	A	N	C	E	D		O	V	E	N
L			G		A		A		W			U
Y	O	G	A		S	P	R	I	N	T	E	D
I			I		T		K		I			G
N	U	A	N	C	E		E		N			E
G		U		A		K	N	I	G	H	T	S
		R		L		I		D		U		
L	E	A	F	L	E	T		E		S		A
E			L		D		Y	A	C	H	T	S
E			A		I		I		U			I
W	O	R	K	A	B	L	E		T	O	A	D
A			E		L		L		E			E
Y	A	R	D		E	N	D	O	R	S	E	S

185

M	A	U	V	E		T		K		S		U
A			I		M	A	R	A	T	H	O	N
Y	O	D	E	L		L		R		A		T
H			W	A	T	C	H	M	A	K	E	R
E		N		N				A		I		U
M	E	A	N	D	E	R	S		K	N	E	E
		U		S		S		A		E		
K	I	S	S		M	I	S	C	A	S	T	S
N		E		O				U		S		E
E	X	A	G	G	E	R	A	T	E			E
A		T		L		E		E	A	S	E	D
D	E	E	P	E	N	E	D		C			E
S		D		S		F		S	H	R	E	D

186

D	Y	N	A	M	I	C		L	O	U	S	E
R			B			H		E		S		D
I		I	S	O	L	A	T	E		U		G
N			E			T		K	N	A	V	E
K	E	N	N	E	L		S			L		
I			T		E	M	E	R	A	L	D	S
N		M			G		V			Y		H
G	R	A	D	U	A	T	E		R			A
		S			L		N	E	A	R	E	D
V	O	C	A	L		G			T			O
E		A		E	U	N	U	C	H	S		W
N		R		A		U			E			E
T	R	A	I	N		S	P	A	R	K	E	D

187

A	R	M	A	D	A		I		V	E	A	L
D			N		V	O	D	K	A		M	
H	U	N	G		E		Y		C	R	A	B
E			L		R	E	L	I	C		T	
R	E	H	E	A	T		L		I	C	E	D
E				S			I		N		U	
S	H	A	N	K	S		C	H	E	E	R	S
	A		U		C				O			E
A	G	E	D		R		B	E	A	M	E	D
	G		I	N	A	N	E		L			A
P	L	U	S		T		A		P	A	C	T
	E		T	I	C	K	S		H			E
U	S	E	S		H		T	H	A	W	E	D

188

M	E	G	A	W	A	T	T		D	A	T	A
A			B		S		O		A			G
L	A	Z	Y		S	M	U	G	G	L	E	R
I			S		E		S		G			E
C	U	R	S	E	S		L		E			E
E		E		A		Y	E	A	R	N	E	D
		D		R		E		N		E		
G	R	O	U	N	D	S		T		E		I
R			N		R		M	I	N	D	E	D
A			W		E		A		A			L
P	H	A	R	M	A	C	Y		K	I	T	E
E			A		M		B		E			R
S	T	O	P		S	T	E	A	D	I	E	S

189

V	I	C	A	R		S		H		H		S
U			R		P	H	E	A	S	A	N	T
L	A	N	C	E		O		T		R		A
G			H	A	N	D	I	C	R	A	F	T
A		M		R				H		N		U
R	O	A	S	T	I	N	G		O	G	R	E
		T		H		U		A		U		
T	U	R	F		S	T	A	P	L	E	R	S
O		I		A				I		S		O
F	L	A	M	B	O	Y	A	N	T			R
F		R		O		E		G	A	P	E	D
E	N	C	I	R	C	L	E		L			I
E		H		T		P		S	K	I	E	D

190

L	I	A	I	S	E	S		D	I	G	I	T
I			N			A		A		E		I
S		H	U	R	R	I	E	D		N		F
T			R			D		S	H	E	L	F
L	E	G	E	N	D		F			T		
E			D		I	N	A	C	T	I	V	E
S		C			V		C			C		X
S	T	A	G	N	A	T	E		T			P
		N			S		T	R	A	U	M	A
T	I	A	R	A		O			C			N
H		S		D	E	P	O	R	T	S		D
A		T		D		T			I			E
T	R	A	M	S		S	T	A	C	K	E	D

191

H	O	L	I	E	R		M		C	L	A	Y
O			M		E	L	A	T	E		M	
V	I	S	A		L		T		L	A	B	S
E			G		A	V	A	I	L		L	
R	E	M	E	D	Y		D		A	X	I	S
E				I			O		R		N	
D	A	M	A	G	E		R	E	S	I	G	N
	U		N				R					O
A	G	O	G		A		L	A	B	E	L	S
	M		R	A	B	B	I		O			I
S	E	M	I		L		T		U	R	G	E
	N		L	E	E	C	H		N			S
S	T	A	Y		S		E	L	D	E	S	T

192

C	A	N	I	S	T	E	R		L	A	I	D
R		R			U		E		E			Y
I	O	T	A		T	E	N	T	A	C	L	E
T		T			U		E		D			I
I	N	F	E	R	S		G		E			N
C		L		A		T	E	A	R	I	N	G
		E		I		R		L		S		
F	R	A	I	L	T	Y		S		L		I
L			M		O		T	O	W	E	L	S
A			P		M		A		A			O
N	U	M	E	R	A	L	S		K	N	O	B
K			D		T		T		E			A
S	A	M	E		O	V	E	R	S	E	E	R

193

A	H	E	A	D		S		R		C		A
N			I		A	M	B	U	S	H	E	D
N	O	B	L	E		U		P		O		A
U			S	T	A	G	G	E	R	I	N	G
A		S		H				E		R		E
L	U	C	K	I	E	S	T		E	B	B	S
		R		C		U		S		O		
O	R	A	L		E	M	P	L	O	Y	E	D
Y		M		F				E		S		E
S	U	B	M	A	R	I	N	E	S			A
T		L		T		N		T	A	P	E	D
E	L	E	G	A	N	C	E		I			E
R		D		L		H		A	L	I	G	N

194

I	S	S	U	I	N	G		B	L	A	N	D
N			P			R		A		F		A
S		A	R	C	H	A	I	C		F		T
T			O			B		K	O	A	L	A
A	B	O	A	R	D		L			I		
N			R		U	N	A	W	A	R	E	S
C		M			P		S			S		Q
E	V	A	C	U	E	E	S		F			U
		L			S		O	R	A	N	G	E
B	R	A	C	E		F			B			E
O		R		D	O	L	L	A	R	S		Z
M		I		I		O			I			E
B	L	A	S	T		P	I	T	C	H	E	D

195

M	O	S	A	I	C		P		H	E	E	L
O			R		L	L	A	M	A		N	
D	O	M	E		I		R		C	I	T	E
E			N		C	R	A	C	K		R	
S	H	R	A	N	K		S		S	T	A	R
T				E			O		A		P	
Y	A	N	K	E	D		L	O	W	E	S	T
	G		I		E			A				I
F	O	W	L		M		C	R	A	N	E	D
	N		L	E	A	S	H		N			I
W	I	D	E		N		E		G	A	T	E
	E		R	I	D	G	E		E			S
A	S	P	S		S		P	U	L	P	I	T

196

B	R	E	A	K	A	G	E		Y	E	L	L
O			M		I		E		E			O
B	O	M	B		S	T	R	O	L	L	E	D
C			E		L		I		L			G
A	C	C	R	U	E		E		O			E
T		O		R		B	R	A	W	L	E	D
		M		N		U		R		A		
B	R	A	I	S	E	S		I		V		R
R			G		T		K	A	R	A	T	E
I			U		C		U		E			T
B	L	E	A	C	H	E	D		C	I	T	Y
E			N		E		O		U			P
S	A	G	A		D	I	S	G	R	A	C	E

197

G	L	O	A	T		A		S		W		L
L			K		E	X	C	A	V	A	T	E
O	R	B	I	T		E		L		T		S
W			N	E	W	S	P	A	P	E	R	S
E		I		L				D		R		E
D	U	M	P	L	I	N	G		A	F	A	R
		M		S		O		I		A		
E	W	E	R		T	W	I	D	D	L	E	D
X		N		R				I		L		E
P	O	S	S	E	S	S	I	O	N			C
O		E		N		E		M	A	L	T	A
S	U	L	T	A	N	A	S		V			D
E		Y		L		T		C	Y	C	L	E

198

Y	A	W	N	I	N	G		M	I	M	E	D
A			E			H		A		A		O
S		O	P	U	L	E	N	T		R		L
H			H			E		E	A	S	E	L
M	Y	S	E	L	F		B			H		
A			W		U	N	A	F	R	A	I	D
K		V			S		K			L		A
S	T	A	M	P	E	D	E		C			W
		G			S		R	O	A	R	E	D
S	C	U	B	A		L			R			L
O		E		M	E	A	S	L	E	S		I
I		S		P		S			E			N
L	O	T	U	S		H	E	R	R	I	N	G

199

C	H	O	S	E	N		O		H	U	R	T
R			K		U	N	C	L	E		E	
U	R	S	A		R		E		F	L	A	T
S			T		S	C	A	N	T		S	
A	P	I	E	C	E		N		I	R	O	N
D				A			I		E		N	
E	A	T	E	R	S		C	A	R	E	S	S
	L		M		T			L				P
B	L	O	B		R		D	E	B	T	O	R
	O		A	G	A	T	E		A			I
T	W	O	S		N		F		T	U	R	N
	E		S	I	D	L	E		O			G
E	D	D	Y		S		R	A	R	E	L	Y

200

S	I	L	E	N	T	L	Y		M	O	O	D
L			X		U		O		O			A
E	P	I	C		C	R	U	M	B	L	E	D
E			E		K		T		I			I
P	S	A	L	M	S		H		L			U
S		Q		U		A	S	C	E	N	D	S
		U		S		I		O		I		
S	L	A	C	K	E	R		P		B		A
H			R		X		C	E	A	S	E	S
A			E		P		A		D			S
D	E	C	A	D	E	N	T		D	I	C	E
E			T		L		E		L			T
D	O	V	E		S	E	R	P	E	N	T	S

SOLUTIONS

201

W	H	E	A	T		A		J		A		E
A			J		A	C	C	U	S	T	O	M
R	U	R	A	L		R		R		T		B
D			R	A	C	E	C	O	U	R	S	E
E		C		M				R		I		D
D	R	A	M	A	T	I	C		I	B	I	S
		T		S		M		L		U		
G	E	A	R		U	P	L	I	F	T	E	D
A		R		G				V		E		O
R	E	A	W	A	K	E	N	E	D			O
N		C		L		E		N	A	M	E	D
E	N	T	R	A	I	L	S		M			L
T		S		S		S		S	P	I	C	E

202

F	L	A	S	H	E	D		R	E	A	C	H
E			E			E		I		R		U
S		S	Q	U	E	A	K	S		C		N
T			U			N		K	N	A	C	K
I	N	T	E	N	D		H			D		
V			L		R	E	A	P	P	E	A	R
A		F			E		R			S		E
L	E	A	K	A	G	E	S		C			D
		N			S		H	E	A	D	E	D
R	E	A	L	M		L			V			E
E		T		U	N	A	R	M	E	D		N
V		I		G		M			R			E
S	E	C	T	S		P	O	I	N	T	E	D

203

V	A	C	A	N	T		O		C	A	T	S
E			O		I	N	C	U	R		R	
S	P	A	R		E		T		A	L	A	S
S			T		R	E	A	R	S		P	
E	Q	U	A	L	S		G		H	E	E	D
L				E			O		E		Z	
S	A	V	A	G	E		N	E	S	T	E	D
	B		S		N			R				A
O	D	E	S		F		U	R	C	H	I	N
	O		I	C	O	N	S		I			G
S	M	O	G		R		H		R	O	L	L
	E		N	I	C	H	E		C			E
A	N	T	S		E		R	E	A	P	E	D

204

C	H	E	A	P		W		L		T		E
O			W		G	R	E	E	D	I	E	R
P	E	C	A	N		E		A		M		A
I			Y	O	U	N	G	S	T	E	R	S
E		E		I				T		P		E
D	E	P	O	S	I	N	G		L	I	A	R
		I		Y		O		R		E		
H	I	D	E		A	D	V	A	N	C	E	D
A		E		S				I		E		A
B	O	M	B	A	R	D	I	N	G			M
I		I		D		U		Y	A	R	N	S
T	A	C	T	L	E	S	S		S			E
S		S		Y		T		G	H	O	U	L

205

G	L	E	A	M	E	D		G	A	U	G	E
R			M			I		A		S		A
U		J	O	S	T	L	E	S		U		S
D			R			L		P	L	A	C	E
G	R	E	A	S	Y		F			L		
I			L		E	X	A	M	P	L	E	S
N		S			A		W			Y		T
G	R	A	N	D	S	O	N		N			O
		T			T		S	T	A	T	I	C
W	E	A	V	E		S			U			K
A		N		A	P	T	N	E	S	S		A
L		I		R		U			E			D
L	O	C	A	L		D	I	S	A	B	L	E

206

I	N	N	A	T	E		A		C	O	A	X
N			B		R	E	B	E	L		L	
S	L	A	B		O		O		E	D	G	Y
U			O		D	E	L	T	A		E	
L	O	A	T	H	E		I		R	O	B	S
T				A			S		E		R	
S	A	L	A	M	I		H	E	R	B	A	L
	M		L		M			G				U
T	O	M	B		P		V	O	C	A	L	S
	R		I	C	I	L	Y		A			T
S	O	W	N		N		I		B	E	E	F
	U		O	R	G	A	N		I			U
A	S	K	S		E		G	E	N	I	A	L

207

H	A	R	M	L	E	S	S		S	O	Y	A
U			I		N		H		I			N
G	R	I	N		S	C	O	R	P	I	O	N
E			T		U		V		H			U
L	E	S	S	E	E		E		O			L
Y		O		C		I	L	L	N	E	S	S
		A		H		V		O		L		
C	U	R	S	O	R	Y		A		S		S
L			A		A		E	F	F	E	C	T
I			L		D		A		U			A
F	A	M	I	L	I	A	R		D	A	U	B
F			N		O		N		G			L
S	I	R	E		S	U	S	P	E	N	S	E

208

M	A	O	R	I		A		R		F		A
A			O		E	X	H	A	L	I	N	G
J	A	M	B	S		L		S		N		R
O			E	N	T	E	R	P	R	I	S	E
R		N		E				S		S		E
S	E	A	F	A	R	E	R		T	H	I	S
		T		K		M		E		I		
P	O	U	R		T	U	R	B	I	N	E	S
E		R		L				O		G		E
T	R	A	D	I	T	I	O	N	S			P
A		L		V		D		Y	A	C	H	T
L	O	L	L	I	P	O	P		P			I
S		Y		D		L		A	S	P	I	C

209

F	O	N	D	E	S	T		O	U	N	C	E
O			A			H		R		O		P
R		R	H	U	B	A	R	B		T		E
E			L			N		S	N	A	R	E
S	A	L	I	V	A		A			B		
E			A		U	M	B	R	E	L	L	A
E		P			R		I			F		N
S	C	A	B	B	A	R	D		C			C
		R			I		E	N	O	U	G	H
J	E	A	N	S		H			W			O
A		G		L	E	A	T	H	E	R		R
I		O		I		N			R			E
L	I	N	E	D		D	R	E	S	S	E	D

210

K	A	Y	A	K	S		A		G	O	A	T
I			N		I	D	L	E	H		B	
M	O	O	D		Z		I		O	P	A	L
O			F		E	X	A	M	S		N	
N	U	R	S	E	S		S		S	U	D	S
O				A			F		E		O	
S	A	F	A	R	I		S	E	D	A	N	S
	W		D		N			G				E
C	A	S	H		N		V	O	I	C	E	D
	K		E	V	A	D	E		M			A
D	E	A	R		R		E		P	A	C	T
	N		E	L	D	E	R		E			E
U	S	E	D		S		S	U	L	K	E	D

211

A	T	L	A	S		S		M		H		A
N			R		S	P	E	A	K	E	R	S
S	I	N	C	E		A		R		L		T
W			S	K	Y	S	C	R	A	P	E	R
E		S		I				Y		F		A
R	E	C	E	N	T	L	Y		L	U	L	L
		R		G		O		M		L		
R	E	A	M		A	P	P	A	L	L	E	D
O		T		B				R		Y		A
W	I	C	K	E	D	N	E	S	S			N
I		H		F		O		H	A	V	O	C
N	E	E	D	I	E	S	T		N			E
G		S		T		E		S	K	I	E	R

212

A	P	P	L	A	U	D		S	L	O	T	H
L			F			A		E		B		O
T		L	E	G	I	B	L	E		T		O
I			R			S		S	T	A	N	D
T	H	R	E	A	D		S			I		
U			D		E	X	A	M	I	N	E	D
D		P			L		F			S		W
E	V	A	C	U	A	T	E		L			A
		R			Y		R	E	A	P	E	R
T	E	A	S	E		P			P			F
H		D		A	M	O	U	N	T	S		I
A		E		R		S			O			N
W	A	D	E	S		Y	E	L	P	I	N	G

213

R	E	G	A	R	D		T		U	N	D	O
E			W		E	X	A	C	T		E	
T	U	B	A		L		R		I	C	E	S
I			R		V	I	G	I	L		P	
R	I	D	D	L	E		E		I	T	E	M
E				I			T		T		N	
S	T	O	L	E	N		S	H	Y	E	S	T
	R		O		O			U				O
W	O	M	B		B		T	E	A	C	U	P
	U		S	O	L	A	R		N			P
K	N	I	T		E		A		G	I	L	L
	C		E	S	S	A	Y		E			E
P	E	A	R		T		S	P	R	E	A	D

214

E	M	B	A	R	K	E	D		O	W	E	D
V			D		I		R		R			I
O	N	C	E		N	E	A	T	N	E	S	S
K			P		G		G		A			C
E	L	A	T	E	S		O		T			O
D		N		V		E	N	D	E	A	R	S
		O		E		L		I		D		
T	A	N	T	R	U	M		R		E		U
H			O		G		A	T	O	N	E	D
R			M		L		D		Z			D
O	R	G	A	N	I	S	M		O	B	O	E
A			T		E		I		N			R
T	A	R	O		R	E	T	R	E	A	D	S

215

R	E	L	A	X		M		G		P		A
I			N		C	O	O	L	N	E	S	S
D	E	A	T	H		T		U		N		T
G			E	I	G	H	T	E	E	N	T	H
E		C		K				S		I		M
D	E	A	F	E	N	E	D		P	L	E	A
		T		D		B		M		E		
F	L	A	W		O	B	S	E	S	S	E	D
A		M		S				R		S		F
B	L	A	N	C	M	A	N	G	E			F
L		R		R		P		E	A	G	L	E
E	M	A	N	A	T	E	S		S			N
S		N		P		X		T	Y	P	E	D

216

F	E	M	A	L	E		F		Y	O	K	E
U			C		W	H	E	R	E		I	
L	O	S	T		E		I		L	A	C	K
L			E		R	E	G	A	L		K	
E	X	O	D	U	S		N		O	M	I	T
S				R			E		W		N	
T	A	L	E	N	T		D	E	S	I	G	N
	V		M		O			A				E
V	E	T	O		B		U	T	E	R	U	S
	R		T	R	A	W	L		N			T
T	A	X	I		C		T		D	I	A	L
	G		O	C	C	U	R		O			E
S	E	E	N		O		A	L	W	A	Y	S

217

C	A	R	A	V	A	N	S		Q	U	I	T
H			L		M		U		U			A
E	T	N	A		E	M	B	L	A	Z	O	N
E			R		N		D		I			K
S	H	A	M	E	D		U		N			E
E		B		T		F	E	A	T	H	E	R
		U		C		I		L		A		
H	A	T	C	H	E	T		T		R		O
O			O		X		R	O	A	M	E	D
W			U		C		E		D			D
L	I	M	P	N	E	S	S		D	O	N	E
E			L		E		T		E			S
D	A	T	E		D	I	S	C	R	E	E	T

218

N	O	O	N	E		O		L		B		A
E			E		I	G	N	I	T	I	N	G
T	R	E	A	D		L		L		L		E
T			R	E	L	E	G	A	T	I	O	N
E		S		T				C		N		T
D	I	A	M	E	T	E	R		E	G	G	S
		N		R		R		O		U		
K	I	D	S		K	E	Y	B	O	A	R	D
E		P		V				O		L		O
E	R	A	D	I	C	A	T	E	D			N
P		P		S		T		S	A	U	N	A
E	L	E	V	A	T	O	R		I			T
R		R		S		P		I	S	S	U	E

219

S	E	A	S	I	C	K		F	E	E	D	S
C			U			N		A		N		O
U		P	L	Y	W	O	O	D		I		U
L			T			W		E	A	G	E	R
P	I	R	A	T	E		A			M		
T			N		J	U	B	I	L	A	N	T
O		A			E		U			S		A
R	E	F	L	E	C	T	S		M			L
		F			T		E	N	A	M	E	L
Y	A	R	D	S		L			R			Y
A		O		U	N	A	W	A	R	E		I
M		N		E		I			E			N
S	I	T	E	D		R	A	I	D	I	N	G

220

R	O	U	N	D	S		F		R	U	I	N
U			I		C	H	A	F	E		M	
N	O	T	E		E		R		E	R	A	S
N			C		N	A	T	A	L		G	
E	X	P	E	C	T		H		I	R	I	S
R				U			E		N		N	
S	A	U	C	E	R		R	A	G	G	E	D
	M		A		I			I				I
H	U	M	P		B		S	L	I	N	K	S
	S		T	A	B	L	E		N			B
S	I	L	O		O		W		P	U	M	A
	N		R	I	N	S	E		U			N
A	G	E	S		S		D	O	T	T	E	D